CLOCK RE

BASICS

STEVEN G. CONOVER

Author of CHIME CLOCK REPAIR and STRIKING CLOCK REPAIR GUIDE

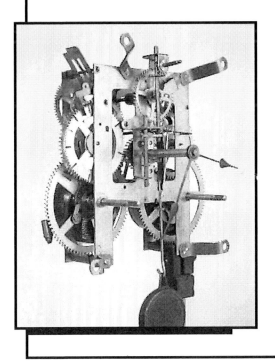

- • **REPAIR PROCEDURES FOR THE BEGINNER**
- • **INFORMATION & SOURCES FOR ALL LEVELS**
- • **TOOLS & EQUIPMENT ILLUSTRATED**
- • **FIVE GREAT "STARTER" CLOCKS FOR REPAIR!**

Books by Steven G. Conover

Repairing French Pendulum Clocks $24.95
How to Repair 20 American Clocks $29.95
Clock Repair Basics $22.95
Clock Repair Skills $24.95
Striking Clock Repair Guide $22.95
Chime Clock Repair $28.50
How to Repair Herschede Tubular Bell Clocks $28.50
Building an American Clock Movement $21.95
How to Make a Foliot Clock $22.95

Clockmakers Newsletter Workshop Series:
Book 1 Repairs $37.95
Book 2 Tools, Tips & Projects $37.95
Book 3 Escapements $34.95
Book 4 Grandfather Clocks $34.95
Book 5 Tubular Bell Clocks $32.95
Book 6 Seth Thomas $37.95
Book 7 Ansonia, Gilbert & Waterbury $37.95
Book 8 Ingraham, New Haven & Sessions $37.95
Book 9 German Clocks $37.95

New books in the *Clockmakers Newsletter Workshop Series* will be announced as they are published.

Steven G. Conover's books are available through our web store: www.clockmakersnewsletter.com.

The books are also available by mail order from:
Clockmakers Newsletter
203 John Glenn Avenue
Reading PA 19607

Also available from clock parts suppliers and Amazon.com.

Cover images: A typical Ingraham movement (left); the company's "Nemo" clock from the 1880's (right).

CLOCK REPAIR
BASICS

STEVEN G. CONOVER

CLOCKMAKERS NEWSLETTER, READING

Dedicated to my wife, Karen

Published by Clockmakers Newsletter
203 John Glenn Avenue
Reading, PA 19607

ISBN 978-0-9624766-5-5

CONTENTS

INTRODUCTION

This book is about basic clock repair. One might think that such a book would logically be done first, followed by other books on increasingly advanced topics. In reality, however, this book is the fifth, not the first, that I have written. The others which came before it covered chime clocks and striking clocks plus specialized instructions on building a clock movement. But first of all came my book, *How to Repair Herschede Tubular Bell Clocks*. It's hard to get more specialized than that.

In a way, this reverse sequence makes sense. There is a great deal of detailed material that *could* be gathered together and included in a basic clock repair text. The real difficulty lies in knowing what to leave out rather than how to fit it all in. For example, there are procedures and formulas clockmakers actually use in their work, and then there are theories that are interesting mostly in an academic way but not practical for everyday tasks.

The research for this book was a constant effort to include only the procedures I actually use in repairing clocks. I have further sharpened the focus of this book by eliminating topics which are not the basic ones the beginner most needs to know. For example, I have included bushing and pivot work because it is a critical part of every job. But I have left pivot replacement for a more advanced book. Why? Repivoting is a specialized, technically difficult topic that will not come up very often for the beginner. The student can get outside help with repivoting in the meantime and take the time to learn it for himself or herself later on, after the basics have been mastered and there are more tools in the workshop.

In writing this book, I have drawn upon my experiences in repairing clocks since the 1970's. I have learned from masters such as Henry Fried, Donald de Carle, and others, by returning often to their books. Some of the information I selected for *Clock Repair Basics* resulted from repairs I completed for articles published in issues of my *Clockmakers Newsletter*. Gradually, I identified the clock repair methods that have become standard for me because they work. These are the ideas brought together for the book.

Clock Repair Basics contains the references I like to have handy myself, all in one volume. You'll find the information I use at the bench: a mainspring length formula; a pendulum length calculation method; and the way to determine the number of beats per hour for a movement. You'll also find, on page 6, a starter list of sources.

Each topic, whether it's letting down mainsprings safely or learning to assemble movements, is presented just as I would teach it to a student in the workshop.

Congratulations! You've picked the most satisfying hobby in the world—and one of the most absorbing careers. Good luck and happy repairing.

Steven G. Conover
Reading, Pennsylvania, August 1996

1

EQUIPMENT & TOOLS

The beginning clock repairer always wants to know what equipment and tools will be needed before he or she can begin to work. This chapter will present a short but necessary list of tools plus a few "wish" items that are very useful.

A beginning repairer who tours a clock repair workshop may come away discouraged after seeing several lathes, a bushing tool, a drill press, a gear cutting outfit, and all kinds of other apparatus. Who would be able to buy all this equipment at once? Which items will he really need to get started? Another beginner might react to the same scene with great excitement, deciding that he should have *everything* he might need before he takes apart that first clock. He may never get around to doing very much repairing—there is always a better lathe or a new milling machine waiting to be discovered. A love affair with tools can become an end unto itself, and it is, after all, a part of clock repairing and clock-making.

The best way for most people to get started is to gather up basic screwdrivers, pliers and other hand tools, most of which he or she owns already, and add a few specialized tools. Then get started repairing! As more experience is gained, individual items of tools and equipment can be purchased as needed.

Look through this chapter and see how easy it is to decide on the tools and equipment to get you started.

Fig. 1. A typical workshop contains many tools and equipment items accumulated over a period of years. This corner of a shop contains a miniature lathe with some accessories, a small milling machine, a mainspring winder, a dial indicator, a micrometer, and a set of Allen wrenches on a stand. The beginner does not need all these items right away.

Fig. 2. A small set of hand tools.

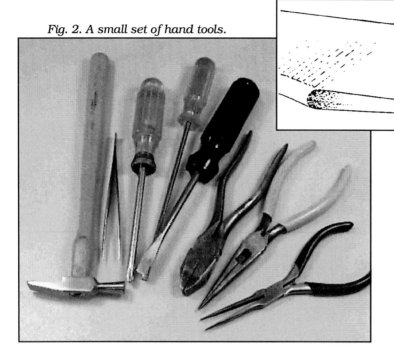

File a slot in a screwdriver blade to make a bending tool for adjusting American strike levers.

Hand Tools

You may already own several screwdrivers. For clock repair you need several of the flat-bladed type and several Phillips screwdrivers. Trying to work on a clock without having a correctly sized screwdriver can cause the blade to slip and damage the screw head.

There are many styles of pliers, but with just a few different ones similar to those shown at the left you can get started on clock repair.

Tweezers and a riveting hammer are also shown.

Let-Down Key

Mainspring-powered clocks cannot be disassembled until the springs are "let down" to an unwound condition. If the plates are separated without neutralizing this power, wheels and other parts will be propelled from the movement. There is almost surely going to be damage to the movement and injury to the repairer. A set of let-down keys allows the safe removal of power. See Chapter 2.

Fig. 3. This let-down key set has three inserts, providing key sizes 5, 6, 7, 8, 10, and 12.

Mainspring Winder

A mainspring winder is one of the most useful tools in the workshop. It is also an item of safety equipment, since it eliminates the more dangerous practice of removing and inserting mainsprings by hand. Always remember that no winder can make it *completely* safe to handle mainsprings, although a good quality winder goes a long way toward that goal. If possible, try several winders before deciding which one to buy. A winder that you don't trust to hold mainsprings safely is a liability.

Fig. 4. Shown: The Keystone mainspring winder.

Fig. 5. A home workshop cleaning station.

Cleaning Equipment

Cleaning is a hotly debated subject. Every repairer has a favorite method for what can only be described as a dirty, time consuming task.

The only equipment absolutely needed for cleaning clocks is one or two plastic tubs with lids and a homemade dryer. The parts to a movement can be immersed in a commercial cleaning solution, soaked briefly, then hand brushed as needed to loosen dirt. One or more rinses are needed to remove the cleaning solution and water from the parts, and then drying is required.

Some repairers use ultrasonic clock cleaning equipment to clean movements faster and more efficiently. Ultrasonic machines are expensive, however, and the beginner who is on a budget would do well to delay the idea of buying one until other equipment items have been added to the workshop. The thing to remember about ultrasonic cleaning is that it does not take the place of disassembly, even though it will clean assembled movements. Almost all movements need to be disassembled for repair.

Chapter 2 presents the basics of clock cleaning.

Bushing Tool

Clock bushings are brass sleeves which are installed to replace worn bearing holes in the plates. A worn hole is reamed out to a diameter which will accept the new bushing, which is then inserted. The reaming can be done with a hand-held reamer, but it is difficult to hold the reamer perpendicular to the clock plate.

A more modern approach is to use a bushing tool for accurate and fast bushing work. The bushing tool is a hand-cranked reaming device which holds the clock plate firmly for perpendicular reaming of the bushing hole. After the hole is completed, a flat pusher is installed in the machine spindle in place of the reamer and used to press or tap the bushing into the hole. There is a range of bushings with various center hole diameters. Two major systems, KWM and Bergeon, have different size reamers and matching bushings. Some bushing tools can work with either system; check before buying.

Bushing work is required in almost every clock movement, so you should consider buying a bushing tool as soon as possible. Chapter 4 describes bushing techniques.

Fig. 6. A Keystone bushing tool.

Basic Lathes

A lathe should be included in a beginner's workshop because pivot work is needed on most clocks. There is simply no way around it, unless someone else does the work for you. Pivots usually need to be polished, and sometimes they need to be cut down to a slightly smaller diameter first to remove deep grooves. Sometimes it is even necessary to cut off a badly damaged pivot and install a new one; this is called *repivoting*. All these pivot operations require a lathe to spin the arbor.

Watchmaker's Lathe

Fig. 7. This watchmaker's lathe is fitted with a counter-shaft to increase motor torque and a set of collets for holding arbors, making it excellent for pivot work.

Miniature Lathe

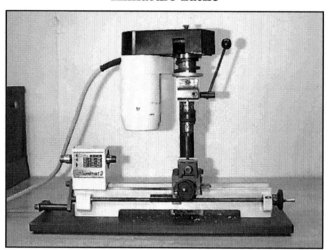

Fig. 8. The Unimat-3 lathe with vertical column installed. (The current model is the Unimat Basic.) Sherline and Cowells are other brands of small lathes available.

A *watchmaker's lathe* is shown in Figure 7. Small and lightweight, it is often found in used equipment sales and is usually fitted with a variable speed, belt driven motor. Clock arbors are quickly set up for pivot polishing or work with the hand graver.

Watchmaker's collets (split chucks) are normally used with these lathes to hold the clock arbors. Numbered collets are available new or used, individually or in sets. The number indicates the size in tenths of a millimeter. For example, a #25 collet holds a piece 2.5 mm in diameter. The clock repairer can make a good start with the even numbers from #10 through #50. Three-jaw chucks are also available for this type of lathe.

Advantages of the watchmaker's lathe are its low initial cost (if purchased used and with few accessories) and its suitability for basic pivot polishing and repivoting.

The main disadvantage of this type of lathe is that a cross slide and other accessories needed for more advanced machining projects are very expensive. It is also difficult to use the watchmaker's lathe to handle the larger diameters of work in the range required for clock repair.

The *miniature lathe* is the single, all-around lathe for most clock repair shops. Figure 8 shows a Unimat-3, out of production since 1990 but relatively easy to find as used equipment. The Unimat can be fitted with a vertical column to temporarily convert it to a small drill press or milling machine.

Most miniature lathes can be fitted to accept watchmaker's collets for holding clock arbors. In addition, a three-jaw chuck enables the repairer to hold a piece of 1/8" to 1" diameter brass or steel rod to be used for making clock parts.

An advantage of the miniature lathe is that it comes equipped (in most cases) with a 3-jaw chuck, cross slide, motor, and other items, enabling the beginner to develop skill in making clock parts such as bushings, rivets, and arbors. Accessories can to be added to the lathe as the repairer plans projects such as gears and pinions.

A disadvantage of the miniature lathe is that it is not as well suited for pivot work as the watchmaker's lathe. Most miniature lathes do not have a handrest for use with a graver, and the available steady rests do not always fit clock arbor and wheel assemblies.

Test Stand

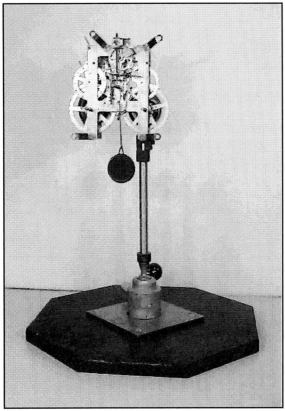

Fig. 9. A test stand for mantel clock movements.

Test stands are essential for your workshop. It's true that some movements can be test-run effectively in their own cases. An example is the schoolhouse clock movement which mounts easily in the case and can be seen fairly well if the dial is left off. At other times this approach is not practical. Some movements are too difficult to install and remove repeatedly, and others may not be visible as they run. Test stands are needed.

The stands come in many shapes and sizes, both homemade and factory produced. It is difficult to repair clocks without at least one bench stand for mantel clock movements and one floor stand for grandfather and certain wall clock movements.

The test stand serves as a support for a movement that is being diagnosed for faults as it runs. When it stops, the movement is completely open to view so the cause of stopping may be seen. The test stand can also enable the clock repairer to turn the hands and watch a strike or chime mechanism that does not work properly. Finally, the stand can hold a movement for a full eight-day run.

Staking Set

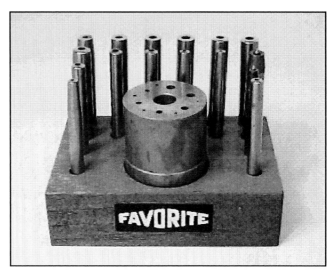

Fig. 10. A clockmaker's staking set.

There are many parts such as wheels and pinions which are driven tightly onto arbors when clocks are made. The parts sometimes need to be separated for repair or replacement. The staking set (Figure 10) contains an anvil with various size holes and a selection of hollow punches. This set is used during riveting. Another of its uses is to support a pivot shoulder as a brass wheel collet or a pinion is driven onto a clock arbor.

Split Stake

The split stake (Figure 11) is useful when a part needs to be staked onto or off an arbor, but the arbor cannot be supported on a pivot shoulder. A brass lantern pinion is an example of an item that requires this kind of support.

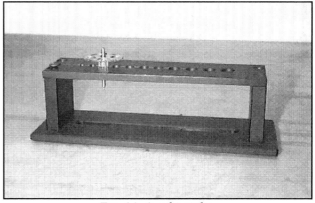

Fig. 11. A split stake.

A Starter List of Sources
Updated 2019

Adams Brown Co., 26 N. Main St., Cranbury NJ 08512, www.adamsbrown.com, 862-217-4508. Dr. Steven Petrucelli. Makers of Timetrax clock timers, sold through Merritt's, Douglassville PA; Timesavers, Scottsdale, AZ; and Adams Brown's eBay store. Also offers high quality antique clocks, including tall case clocks.

Black Forest Imports, Inc. info@blackforestimports.com, 714-637-4307. This supplier has warehouses on the East and West Coasts and offers German movements and parts for modern-era clocks including grandfather, mantel, wall, and cuckoo styles.

Blue Ridge Machinery & Tools, Inc., Hurricane, WV, www.blueridgemachinery.com, 1-800-872-6500. Metalworking tools and accessories, including Sherline lathes and parts for Unimat 3 & 4 lathes.

Conover, Steven G., www.clockmakersnewsletter.com. Author and publisher of books on clock repair and clockmaking. See the inside front cover of this book for a list of the titles.

MSC Industrial Direct Co., Inc., www.mscdirect.com, 1-800-645-7270. This supplier provides a full line of machinery, tools, and metals. A company catalog is available online.

Merritt's, Douglassville, PA, www.merritts.com, 610-689-9541. Merritt's offers clock and watch supply items, clock repair tools, movements, and books. The company publishes a catalog. In addition, Merritt's maintains a clock shop with hundreds of antique clocks on display, ideal for collecting or for restoration projects.

National Association of Watch & Clock Collectors (NAWCC), 514 Poplar St., Columbia, PA 17512, www.nawcc.org, 717-684-8261. National club membership brings access to local chapters, the National Watch & Clock Museum (also open to the public), and the Library & Research Center in Columbia, PA. In addition, NAWCC's web site features an online forum for clock repair enthusiasts and collectors.

Timesavers, Scottsdale, AZ, www.timesavers.com 1-800-552-1520. This supplier has clock parts, clock repair tools, movements, and books. The company publishes a catalog.

2

DISASSEMBLY & CLEANING

Only the cheapest kind of movement, found in an unworn condition, should be cleaned while still assembled and called "repaired". That kind of clock doesn't turn up very often. It will be necessary to safely disassemble and thoroughly clean almost every movement.

This chapter covers practical considerations, including some safety tips, for the novice repairer who is ready to take apart and clean a movement. It seems hardly necessary to state that the pendulum, hands, and dial should be carefully removed and set aside as the work is started. An early step for grandfather and most other weight driven clocks is the removal of the weights. For spring driven mantel and wall clocks, it is usually necessary to remove certain screws to permit the removal of the movement from the case. An introductory book such as this one cannot possibly list in detail all the various types of movements with their different methods of hand and dial attachments. You must be careful to remove these parts without forcing them. Be especially careful of the dial.

Minute hand attachments include taper pins which are pressed out with pliers; threaded nuts to be unscrewed; flat, square washers which are removed by turning them about 45°; and pressed-on minute hands.

Hour hands are normally held to the hour tube with a slotted brass bushing which is part of the hand assembly. A twisting, pulling action is often the best way to remove the hand, but be careful not to pull too hard—if the hour hand bushing remains stuck to the hour pipe, you will be pulling the hour wheel strongly against the washer which holds it in place. Continued pulling may cause damage to the movement. The problem may be that the brass sleeve is corroded to the hour pipe. A small drop of oil, allowed to set for an hour, may loosen it.

Dials are sometimes mounted to the case, but more often they are pillar-mounted directly to the movement. Removing three or four taper pins or nuts will permit the dial to be taken off. Look carefully and don't remove the wrong pins—the ones that hold the clock movement plates together!

Pendulums do not need much discussion at this stage. They are unhooked and set aside to prevent scratching or other damage and to save the suspension spring from breakage.

Letting Down the Power

One of the first concerns of the repairer is to identify the type of power (spring or weight) and determine how this power should be safely released or contained. This section covers the procedure for releasing several types of power.

Weight Driven Movements. It is usually a simple matter to unhook and remove the weights from a

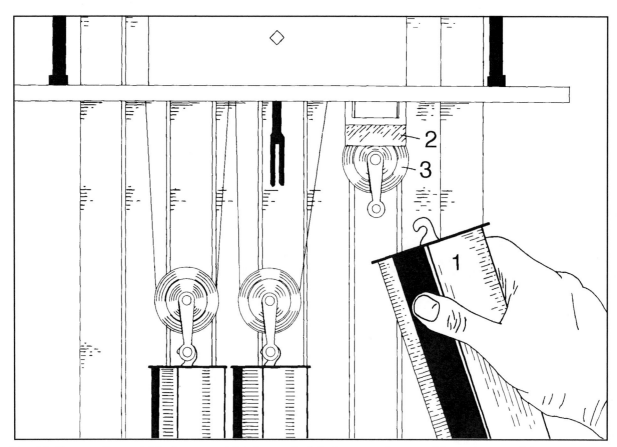

Fig. 12. Remove the weights from a weight-driven clock before you disassemble any parts of the movement. Use soft cotton gloves or a cloth to grip each weight (1). Herschede movements were originally shipped with wooden pulley blocks (2) to prevent tangling of the cables. On most clocks, each weight has a pulley (3).

movement. Figure 12 shows this being done to a Herschede tubular bell movement. Brass weight cables are often springy, and as the weight is taken off, the coils expand, slip off the end of the cable drum, and get caught behind wheels or wrapped around arbors. It can be quite a mess to unravel. In Figure 12 a specially-made Herschede wooden block has been placed over the pulley. The winding key is turned until the block contacts the underside of the seatboard.

A more common way to prevent tangled cables in most movements is to have someone remove the weight while you keep a slight downward pressure on the pulley or weight hook. You may be able to do all of this yourself, but some weights are very heavy and you have to be able to set the weight down safely. With the weight out of the way, you can release the click (Figure 13), pulling downward on the cable to unwrap it from the drum.

Spring Driven Movements. Extra caution is required with spring driven clocks because of the power of the mainsprings. These springs, some of which are over eight feet long, can injure you if they are allowed to escape in an uncontrolled manner. Damage to the movement is also likely.

Before considering safe ways to let down several types of mainsprings, we need to look at the click and the ratchet wheel. These are the parts that hold back the power of the spring and allow it to be wound up with a key. Figure 13 shows that the ratchet wheel has angled teeth to allow the pawl, called a click by repairers, to engage and hold it after each turn of the winding key. The click spring returns the click to the seated position in a positive manner. This, of course, makes the distinctive clicking sound as a clock is wound. Letting down a mainspring is much more difficult than winding one up.

Barreled mainsprings are the simplest to let down. The barrel and main wheel act as a self-contained unit to power the clock. The barrel is also a tube that restrains the spring when it is let down. To release a barreled mainspring, place the let-down key on the arbor and turn it a small amount—less than one "click"—in the winding direction to relieve the pressure on the click. Still holding the let-down key firmly, pry up the click against the click spring pressure. When the click is completely free of the ratchet wheel, hold it there and lessen your grip on the key, allowing it to spin slowly in your hand. In a few moments the mainspring will be let down and

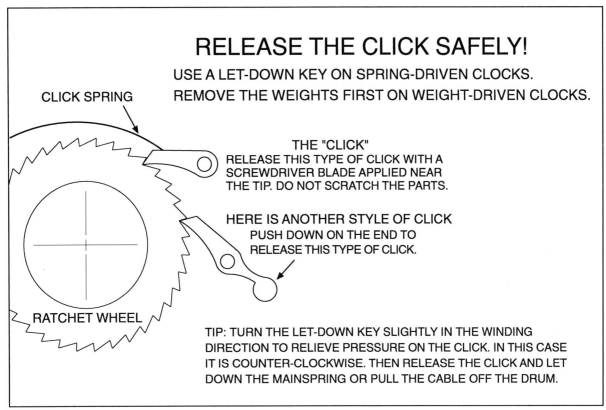

RELEASE THE CLICK SAFELY!
USE A LET-DOWN KEY ON SPRING-DRIVEN CLOCKS.
REMOVE THE WEIGHTS FIRST ON WEIGHT-DRIVEN CLOCKS.

CLICK SPRING

THE "CLICK"
RELEASE THIS TYPE OF CLICK WITH A
SCREWDRIVER BLADE APPLIED NEAR
THE TIP. DO NOT SCRATCH THE PARTS.

HERE IS ANOTHER STYLE OF CLICK
PUSH DOWN ON THE END TO
RELEASE THIS TYPE OF CLICK.

RATCHET WHEEL

TIP: TURN THE LET-DOWN KEY SLIGHTLY IN THE WINDING
DIRECTION TO RELIEVE PRESSURE ON THE CLICK. IN THIS CASE
IT IS COUNTER-CLOCKWISE. THEN RELEASE THE CLICK AND LET
DOWN THE MAINSPRING OR PULL THE CABLE OFF THE DRUM.

Fig. 13. The "click" is the clockmaker's term for the metal pawl which locks in the teeth of the ratchet wheel to hold back the power of the mainspring or weight. Plan ahead on how to release the click safely.

restrained safely within the barrel. After releasing the mainspring this way (there may be one, two, or three mainsprings in your clock), it is safe to separate the plates.

The let-down mainspring is safely bound within the barrel tube, and the barrel cover could be removed at any time. It is, however, important to understand that the mainspring is by no means uncoiled and without power. Although it is possible to take the barrel out of the movement now so that the rest of the movement can be disassembled, just remember that the mainspring still needs to be taken out of the barrel for cleaning and inspection. That procedure will be described in Chapter 3.

As always, there are exceptions. A few barrels have a stop-works mechanism attached to the barrel wheel to even out the utilization of the spring. Look for an odd-shaped gear and pawl attached to the face of the barrel wheel. When the mainspring is let down, it may be possible to remove the barrel from the movement. This kind of barrel still has power locked up in the spring that must be let down before the barrel cover is removed and work proceeds further. This requires special procedures which may vary from one such barrel to the next.

Fig. 14. This mainspring was let down within its barrel and the cover removed to show the coils of the spring.

Another special case of the barreled mainspring is the fusee. As shown in Figure 15, the fusee is a tapered cone connected with a cable or chain to the mainspring barrel. The fusee gives less mechanical advantage to the mainspring when the spring is fully wound and more advantage as it winds down. This evens out the variation in power during the run of the clock.

Only one aspect of the fusee clock concerns us in this chapter—letting the mainspring down safely. The clock is wound at the fusee arbor, never at the barrel arbor. The mainspring cannot, however, be let down at the fusee. Unfortunately, it is not safe to let the spring down at the barrel arbor, either; fusee mainsprings are very strong, and the squared ends of the barrel arbor are often too short for a let-down key to hold back the spring. The click on the barrel arbor will probably not even have a click spring to seat the click in the ratchet teeth!

The best procedure is to begin by letting the clock run down as far as possible. Even if there is no apparent power left to the fusee wheel at this point, there is still power left in the mainspring barrel.

Fig. 15. The fusee requires special treatment.

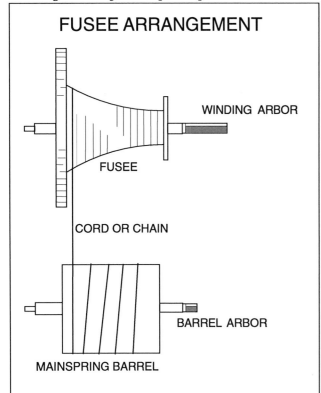

FUSEE ARRANGEMENT

WINDING ARBOR

FUSEE

CORD OR CHAIN

BARREL ARBOR

MAINSPRING BARREL

THE CLOCK IS WOUND WITH THE WINDING ARBOR, NOT THE BARREL ARBOR. THE MOVEMENT IS GENERALLY ALLOWED TO RUN DOWN TO RELEASE THE SPRING. EVEN AT THIS POINT THERE IS STILL POWER LEFT IN THE MAINSPRING—ABOUT ONE TURN OF THE BARREL ARBOR. THIS LAST TURN CAN BE LET DOWN AT THE BARREL ARBOR. THIS LOWER WINDING SQUARE IS OFTEN VERY SHORT AND DIFFICULT TO GRIP.

Fig. 16. The click, click spring and ratchet wheel in an American open-mainspring design. The mainspring has been removed from the wheel for this photo.

This is because the clock is set up with at least one turn of the mainspring arbor when the clock is assembled. Now it is necessary to install a let-down key on the barrel arbor and let down this last turn—or more—until the power is completely neutralized. It is only because of the powerful spring and the usually short-ended barrel arbor that the spring is not simply let down all the way from a fully wound condition. Do it the safe way!

Open mainsprings are the most common mainspring arrangement found in American clocks of the 19th and 20th centuries. The mainspring end is fitted with a loop fastener which fits over a movement pillar. Before this spring can be let down, it must be wrapped with wire or a mainspring retainer purchased from a clock supplier. The retainer is just a loop of stiff wire which extends about three-quarters of the way around the spring.

Wind the mainspring until it is small enough in diameter for the retainer to fit around it. Place the let-down key onto the squared end of the winding arbor. Turn less than one "click" in the winding direction, to take the pressure off the click, then pry up the tip of the click. Hold the click away from the ratchet wheel as you allow the smooth handle of the let-down key to spin in your hand in a controlled manner. This lets down the mainspring within the retainer. To make sure the mainspring is fully let down, push once or twice on the mainspring coils to separate any coils of the dirty mainspring that may be stuck together. Figure 16 shows the appearance of the ratchet and click in an open-mainspring movement.

As with the barreled mainspring, the open spring is now safe to handle and remove from the movement. It must still be removed from the retainer for cleaning. Chapter 3 will explain how this can be done. Read the sections of Chapter 3 which apply before cleaning a movement.

Separating the Movement Plates

Once the mainsprings are contained, disassembling a movement is next. Remove the pillar nuts or taper pins and carefully separate the plates. Most of the arbors can be removed easily. A few items, such as gathering pallet arbors, will remain with one of the plates unless the gathering pallet or other part is removed. If the part is held with a pin or is relatively easy to remove, then you should remove it. A part which is firmly staked on is another matter. An example is the center arbor of a modern German movement. The cannon pinion is staked on so tightly that a special procedure is required to remove it. Unless there is a worn pivot hole or some other compelling reason to take off the cannon pinion and remove the center arbor from the front plate, leave it there. It will not get in the way of the cleaning operation.

If you are not familiar with the movement you are repairing, you might

Fig. 17. The parts to be cleaned can be placed in a steel mesh basket. Don't forget the mainsprings. (See Chapter 3 for more on mainsprings.)

want to sketch a few of the relationships of the parts before removing all the parts from the plates. Some repairers take photos or video footage of a movement.

Two wheels may look very much the same in some movements. You can consider scratching an identification such as "T" for time train on a wheel. The mark should be small, neat, and in an inconspicuous place. Some repairers will object to marking gears or other parts. I suppose it is a practice more easily justified in a modern, factory-produced movement. Marking parts would be harmful to a valuable movement. You will soon see the kinds of marks other repairers have made before you. Don't go by someone else's marking system unless you are certain it is correct. There is no reason to mark every wheel in a clock like this: T1, T2, and so on.

Individual repairers have different procedures for disassembly. They may string related parts, such as strike train wheels, on a loop of soft wire to keep them together. Others just carefully place the parts in a cleaning basket. This brings us to one of the most disputed areas in clock repair: cleaning procedures.

CLEANING CLOCK MOVEMENTS

Any clock cleaning method should:
- Be as safe as possible
- Remove dirt and oil
- Brighten parts
- Not stain the movement
- Not remove lacquer, if any is present
- Not cause rust

There are two main types of clock cleaning solutions: water-based solutions that typically contain ammonia; and petroleum-based solutions that do not contain any water.

Some people feel that the water-based solutions do a better job of brightening the parts. You should carefully read the manufacturer's instructions about safe use. Hot water can be used to rinse the cleaning solution off the parts. Some repairers use compressed air to drive off most of the water at this stage.

Whether or not water is used as a first rinse, a commercial clock rinse solution should be used at the end to remove all water and prevent rusting of the parts. Finally, the parts are dried with hot air. Find out the proper way to dispose of used water-based solutions in your area.

Consider the petroleum-based type of solution next. The advantage is that, without water, there is little chance that the act of cleaning will create conditions that will cause rust on steel parts. On the downside, the cleaning solution may have a strong solvent smell. It is especially important to follow the manufacturer's instructions and cautions about its use. You also have to find out about local regulations covering the disposal of used solution. After cleaning, you must use a rinse solution to remove the cleaning solution from the parts. The sequence is still cleaning, rinsing, and drying.

There are many issues involved in the safe use of cleaning solutions. These include protecting the skin, using proper ventilation, and avoiding the hazards of flammable materials. I cannot advise the clock repairer how to best protect him or herself. Read the labels and ask questions, then do what is best and safest for you.

It is little consolation that ten clockmakers placed in the same room would probably describe at least eight different methods for cleaning clocks. Here are some of the principles which should be important to all of them.

A Cleaning Procedure

Disassemble the movement as much as possible, using the guidelines in the previous section. Always remove bridges and cocks to prevent solution from seeping underneath and forming a slimy residue. There are always some decisions to make about disassembly. Take apart a grandfather clock main wheel assembly if it is held together with a tension washer and a screw. If, on the other hand, it is riveted together or held with a "one-way" split washer, clean it as-is, assembled.

Select containers for your solutions. Plastic containers such as the Rubbermaid "Rough Tote" shown in Figure 18 are good for most solutions, but any container should be tested to make sure it will withstand your particular solution without softening or cracking. The container pictured is partially filled with an ammoniated cleaner. A tight lid may prevent evaporation, but it is up to you to consider the issue of fumes and evaporation for your own safety. Some repairers have two containers of cleaner and two rinses. Most of their movements go through a bath in the "dirty" cleaner to remove the worst of

Fig. 19. A wooden box can be made into a clock parts dryer. Dryers are also available from clock suppliers.

A hair dryer rests on top of the box and blows air in through the top.

the grease and oil from the parts. The better solution is used next, then the "dirty" rinse and finally the clean rinse. Eventually the dirty solutions are disposed of and the other solutions take their places; new solutions then become the clean solutions. This may reduce your cost for solutions. Other repairers use an entirely different type of cleaner to remove dirt from the worst movements, instead of using two of the same cleaners and two rinses.

Soak the parts for a few minutes, but remember that your solution may remove the lacquer, if any is present, after a longer period. A hand brush may be used to loosen dirt from the parts. Use protective gloves to keep the solutions off your hands.

Rinse the parts next. If you use a water-based cleaner, you may want to rinse it off with hot tap water that is not too hot to handle safely. You should follow this first rinse with a non-ammoniated rinse to remove the water. If you skip the step of removing the water with a solution, you will have to carefully hand-dry and hot-air dry the parts. Some repairers say rust will follow, no matter how carefully you dry the parts. It's certainly true that water does remain in hidden areas such as the threaded holes in brass movement pillars. When steel screws are put back in these holes, serious rusting occurs.

Dry the parts. Clock dryers are available from clock suppliers. You can also make your own dryer. Figure 19 shows a homemade dryer made from a wooden box. The front is hinged as a door and held shut with a simple hook. The floor of the box has a border of molding nailed to it and screening stretched across to make a raised screen floor. This helps in the circulation of air and prevents the parts

Fig. 18. Buy two sturdy containers like this one for your cleaning solutions or rinses (see text).

from resting in pooled solution. The hot air is provided by an old-fashioned hair dryer; the hose is inserted into a hole in the top of the box.

Ultrasonic Cleaning

Many high-volume clock repair shops (and some hobbyists, too) use ultrasonic clock cleaning machines to speed up the cleaning process. Those who have come to depend upon these machines would not want to return to hand cleaning methods. For the beginner, however, it is best to start with basics by cleaning manually. As the volume of repairs increases along with the repairer's budget, the ultrasonic cleaner is worth considering. Clock suppliers' catalogs will give those who are interested a better idea of the sizes and costs of the machines.

Some Thoughts on Disassembly and Cleaning

The purpose of this chapter has been to progress from a dirty clock to one that is clean and ready to be repaired. The whole subject of how one gets from one point to the other is filled with varying opinions. There is no single correct approach that is right to the exclusion of all others.

Some repairers dislike even taking clock movements apart to clean them. They are either afraid to tackle the work or unwilling to spend the time to do it right. The argument is sometimes heard that one cannot repair profitably if too much time is spent on disassembling every clock. There is a grain of truth here: the seasoned repairer knows how to save time by avoiding procedures that do not need to be done. These may be called shortcuts or time savers, according to your point of view. An example is the cleaning of a hammer assembly, perhaps ultrasonically, and removing any water added during the process. If the assembly ends up clean, there would have been no point in taking it apart and spending the extra time sorting, finding, and reassembling all the hammers, washers, and other parts of the assembly.

There are many cleaning methods that can be used after deciding how far to disassemble a movement (and I maintain that complete disassembly is the norm). Try some different solutions and keep safety as a top priority. You will discover the method that is right for you.

MORE ABOUT MAINSPRINGS

Handling mainsprings is an especially difficult task for the beginning repairer who does not own a mainspring winder. In this chapter, safe let-down procedures for barreled mainsprings and open mainsprings have been covered. The springs are not ready for cleaning, however, unless they have been further released to a fully open position. This permits cleaning solutions and rinses to penetrate the coils and later be dried; it also allows the repairer to wipe the coils if desired. *Fully releasing a mainspring requires a mainspring winder and is detailed in the next chapter.*

If you have let down a mainspring within its barrel, set it aside until you read Chapter 3 and decide how to approach these springs. The beginner should have an experienced repairer remove the mainspring from the barrel or consider just leaving the spring in the barrel and not cleaning it. Removal by hand is dangerous; reinsertion by hand is even more so.

Fig. 20. If there is no winder available, you can let open-type mainsprings down to this extent and then clean the entire assembled movement.

Fortunately, there is an approach you can take with some open mainsprings if you do not have a mainspring winder. First, look at the springs. If either one is rusty or cracked, it should be replaced. Place a retainer on it now, and after disassembly, just unhook the mainspring inner end from the arbor hook and set the spring aside in its wire retainer.

If, on the other hand, one or both open mainsprings are usable, they can be cleaned in the movement. Use a let-down key and release the springs until the coils are open as shown in Figure 20. You can now clean the entire movement with the springs in it. Do not use a water-based cleaner for this job unless you rinse with a solution that removes the water from the parts. After the parts are dry, wind the mainsprings up and install retainers on the mainsprings; then let the springs down within the retainers. Disassemble the movement for repair.

3

MAINSPRINGS & WEIGHTS

In the previous chapter we covered the safe let-down of a clock's power. This was a necessary first step before the movement plates could be separated and the parts removed for cleaning. The repairer still needs more basic information about the care and handling of mainspring and weight power.

We will begin with mainsprings. For each type of spring there is some kind of restraint that holds it to a manageable coiled diameter. In the case of the barreled spring, the barrel itself is the restraint; in the case of the open, loop end mainspring, a retainer or a piece of wire is wrapped around the spring to control it. We will also look at a "mainspring box", a barrel-like retainer that is fixed to the movement plate, making the power unit a combination of the barreled and open loop-end types. Once completely free of all retainers or restraints, mainsprings can be cleaned and checked for rust, torn ends, and other damage.

Removing Barreled Mainsprings

A mainspring contained in a barrel should be removed, inspected, cleaned, reinserted in the barrel, and lubricated. In some cases a cracked outer end is cut off and a new hole end is made. At other times, a rusty or weak mainspring is replaced with a new one. The new mainspring is matched as closely as possible to the width, thickness, and length of the old one. This section covers all these topics plus the use of a mainspring winder to handle

a spring safely.

After a mainspring is let down within the barrel as explained in Chapter 2, the barrel is removed from the clock. It is now a self-contained power unit (Figure 21) which needs further servicing.

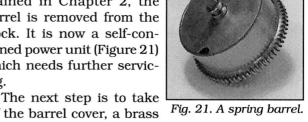

The next step is to take off the barrel cover, a brass *Fig. 21. A spring barrel.* disk which is a press-in or snap fit in a recess in the barrel tube. There are two ways to remove a cover. The first is to rap the end of the arbor *oppo-*

Fig. 22. A barrel with the cover removed.

site the cover onto a wood block. Most barrels have the cover at the front end, so the back end of the arbor would be tapped against the wood. If this does not dislodge the cover, then take a narrow screwdriver blade and insert it in the slot which is present in most covers. Prying off the cover this way will cause a small injury to the edge of the barrel, but normally the cover is replaced in the same orientation each time and there is just one marked spot from the blade.

With the cover off, the mainspring coils can be seen as in Figure 22. The next step is to remove the spring from the barrel. This is best done with a mainspring winder. If you do not have a mainspring winder, it is better in most cases to leave the dirty spring in the barrel than to pull it out with pliers. Pulling out the mainspring exposes you to danger from the spring if it flies out of the barrel, and the spring coils may be stretched into a helix as they are pulled out of the barrel. In the rare cases when my mainspring winder will not fit a spring, I first unhook and remove the barrel arbor. Then, wearing heavy work gloves and eye protection, I use pliers to ease out the center coils of the spring. Then it is just a matter of unwinding the spring, coil by coil, until the hole end is reached at the barrel hook.

Some texts describe another procedure whereby a blanket is draped over your hands, arms, and the spring barrel (to protect your face). The pliers are given a twist in the winding direction, and the spring is extracted from the barrel in one continuous motion. Even if you do get the mainspring out without problems, you will still have to wind it back into the barrel *by hand* later on. That effort requires a lot of strength in the hands and could result in serious cuts or other injuries. That's why I strongly recommend using a mainspring winder for removing and inserting mainsprings.

There are several different patterns of mainspring winders on the market. Try as many as you can

Fig. 23. A mainspring barrel is mounted on a Keystone mainspring winder. The winder is held in a vise.

before making a decision on which one to buy. Figure 23 shows a Keystone mainspring winder being used to remove a mainspring. With the tool set up as shown, the barrel is held in the clamp with rubber-lined jaws, and the spindle chuck is fastened onto the winding arbor of the barrel. Note the notched sleeve resting on the spindle of the tool. The crank is turned to wind up the spring, and then the sleeve is placed over the mainspring. The crank

Fig. 24. These mainsprings have been removed with a mainspring winder and have expanded to their full size. They can now be cleaned and inspected.

is firmly held in the hand and allowed to unwind slowly, letting the mainspring down within the sleeve. The hole-end of the spring is released from the barrel hook, and the clamp and barrel are taken off the tool and set aside. Now you are left with the hole-end of the spring projecting out of the notch in the sleeve. This unit is placed on the winder, wound up again, and the sleeve is removed. Finally the spring is carefully let down to its full size. This process normally takes only a few minutes. Following the manufacturer's instructions and proceeding very deliberately will help to insure your safety. Reinstalling a mainspring is the reverse of the procedure just described.

Inspecting a Hole-End (Barreled) Mainspring

Once it is safely out of the barrel, the mainspring will look like the examples shown in Figure 24. The mainspring can now be inspected, and if it is rusty, it should be replaced. A rusty spring will not work smoothly even if an attempt is made to polish off the rust, and the spring is far more likely to break in service than a spring with no rust.

The next area to check is the hole-end of the spring. This section is flexible, softened steel which is subject to repeated bending as the mainspring is wound up and run down again. The end strains against the barrel hook, often causing cracks to develop around the hole in the spring. Sometimes these cracks can be seen only with an eye loupe.

They are the warning signs that something must be done now to repair or replace the spring. To put a spring back in the barrel with a cracked end is to guarantee a failure at some time in the future. If the end breaks out of the spring when it is fully wound, there is likely to be damage to gears and pinions in the clock. One remedy is to replace any mainspring which has a cracked end. This places a new, full-strength spring in the clock and makes further problems less likely.

Sometimes it is decided that instead of replacing the spring, the damaged end of the old spring will be cut off and a new hole made. It is often possible to shorten a mainspring one time only, by about an inch, without shortening the run time of the clock too much. For example, a clock which ran a full seven days and twelve hours of the eighth day might now run only six hours into the eighth day. To shorten a mainspring, first soften an additional portion of the spring by holding the damaged end in a propane torch flame and watching the dark

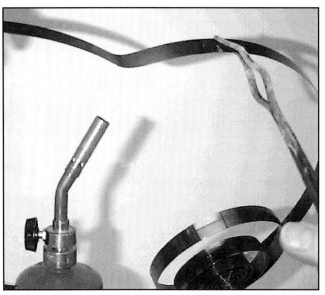

Fig. 25. Before shortening a mainspring, heat the steel to soften it in the area to be cut (see the text on this page).

color "walk" about an inch up the mainspring. Figure 25 shows this being done to an extra-long, new mainspring which is being shortened to fit in a barrel, but the principle is the same. After allowing the spring to cool, use a hacksaw to cut off the damaged end. Round off the end to match the original end, and then remove the sharp edges. To make the new hole in the softened end of the spring, you may be able to use a hand-held punch which is sold for that purpose.

My method for making the new hole end is shown in Figure 26. Place the cut-off original end over the new mainspring end. Use a heavy felt-tip pen to trace the outline of the original hole, which will be

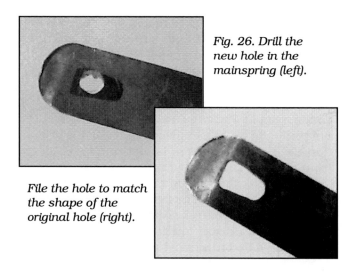

Fig. 26. Drill the new hole in the mainspring (left).

File the hole to match the shape of the original hole (right).

elongated rather than round, onto the steel. Prick-punch a dimple into the spring at a location estimated to be the center of the hole. Clamp the mainspring end in a vise, backed up with a piece of scrap 1" x 2" wood. Use a hand drill with a bit as large as possible to stay within the drawn shape. Drill through the steel at the location marked with the punch and then remove the wood piece. Clamp the spring end again and use various flat and round needle files to reach the desired shape. Matching the original shape will help to assure that the mainspring end will fit properly on the barrel hook. Above all there must not be any sharp corners within the shape of the new hole. Any corner will become a crack after a period of time. Remove all sharp edges. Use pliers to create a slight bend required in the end to match the bend in the old end of the spring. This creates the correct angle for attaching to the barrel hook.

Figure 27 shows the portion that was cut off an extra-long new mainspring to fit a barrel. If the calculation calls for a 70" long mainspring and it is necessary to purchase one that is 74" long, just cut

Fig. 27. This new mainspring was too long as received and was shortened by several inches to fit a barrel.

4" off the end and make a matching hole-end as described. Note how the holes in the old and new ends are a close match.

Another problem mainspring which should be replaced is a "tired" or weak spring. It is difficult to define exactly what is meant by these terms, but

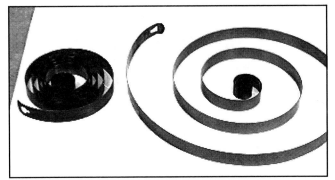

Fig. 28. The mainspring on the left is an old one removed from a barrel. The mainspring on the right is new.

Figure 28 will help to illustrate. The old mainspring on the left has a much reduced capability, as shown by the fact that when fully released it is not much larger in diameter than a barrel. In contrast, the spring on the right is new and has never been in a barrel before. It expands to a large diameter. This is not to say that good springs will always look like this one when they are removed from barrels for cleaning and inspection. I have verified that a new spring will be somewhere between the extremes shown in Figure 28 if it is removed from the clock after a test period. Experience will teach you to recognize which springs are weak and which ones are not. One of the most pointed lessons is learned by cleaning and reusing an old spring which looks questionable, only to have it run a clock for six days instead of eight. The entire movement may have to be dismantled to permit the replacement of the spring with a new one. Some repairers replace almost every mainspring in the clocks they repair. Although that is not my policy, I can understand why some people approach mainsprings that way.

Ordering a Hole-End Mainspring

Selecting a replacement barreled mainspring is sometimes as easy as measuring the old one. As a convenience for repairers, most supply catalogs list mainspring dimensions in English and metric units. I prefer to use a micrometer to measure the thickness in thousandths of an inch and a scale to measure the width in millimeters. For length I use inches.

Thickness of a mainspring must be correct within close limits. A mainspring of .012" thickness is a relatively weak spring, the type used in small French movements. By increasing the thickness by just

.006", we arrive at the powerful springs used in much larger movements. Thickness becomes a compromise when you cannot find the exact mainspring you need in suppliers' catalogs. My approach is to avoid using a stronger mainspring than the one which came out of the clock unless I know it was too weak a spring. A spring of .018" thickness can wear out the gears in an old movement if the correct spring was .016". Backing up this general approach is the idea that today's mainsprings have more torque than 100-year-old mainsprings of equal thickness had when they were new.

Width of a mainspring is a little less critical than thickness. If the only available mainspring of the correct thickness and length is 1 mm narrower than the original spring, this does not usually present a problem. A wider mainspring cannot be used because it will not allow the barrel cover to fit securely, and in addition, there will be no endshake, or freedom, in the fit of the barrel arbor.

Length of an old mainspring can be measured directly if you try to stretch it out, although there is some estimating involved because of the tight inner coils. You can also measure the inner diameter of the barrel and compare it to the "diameter" figure included in suppliers' mainspring tables. This figure represents the coiled diameter of the wire-bound mainsprings as they are shipped to you. If the coiled diameter fits in your barrel, it is close to the correct length.

It is far better to use the formula below to find the correct length mainspring for your barrel. This gives you an exact length for the spring of your chosen thickness that will turn the barrel the maximum number of times. This is an important concept because a mainspring which is too short will obviously give a reduced number of barrel turns. It is equally true that a mainspring which is too long will not give the maximum number of possible turns because it fills up some of the empty space in the barrel required for winding and unwinding. The formula is based on the idea that a mainspring occupies only a part of the available space in the barrel. For a barrel to be able to deliver the maximum number of turns possible with a mainspring of a speci-

---

Mainspring Length in Five Steps

1. Inside diameter of barrel, squared, times .7854
2. Diameter of arbor, squared, times .7854
3. Subtract step #2 from step #1
4. Divide by 2
5. Divide by the mainspring thickness

---

fied thickness, the spring should occupy one half the available area. A look back at Figure 22 will show this concept. Naturally, the area varies with the diameter of the barrel. Area also varies with the diameter of the barrel arbor, since the arbor takes away from the area available to the mainspring. I use the formula on page 17, which has been expressed as five steps. This method, which agrees with other sources I have read, was a procedure used by Givler Gear, a firm of gear cutters, and submitted to *Clockmakers Newsletter* by H.C. Hartzell in 1989.

If you suspect that an old mainspring you wish to replace is not the correct thickness for the clock, you will have to make a judgment based on similar clocks. Thicknesses will fall mostly between .012" for small, round French movements, moving upward in roughly .001" increments to .018" and even beyond for larger clocks. Exact replacement mainsprings are available for some modern-era clocks such as Hermle. Unfortunately, educated guesses and a few compromises will be part of your selection process.

An overall approach to replacing a barreled mainspring starts with measuring the thickness and width of the old spring. If you have no reason to disregard these measurements, you can proceed to use the formula to calculate the correct length of mainspring for your barrel. This takes away all guesswork and may even provide a better fit than the mainspring you are replacing. Next, go to a clock supplier's mainspring table and find the selection of hole-end mainsprings in your width. Then look for the required thickness and finally the length. There may be a need to compromise in order to select an available mainspring. My approach is to consider a mainspring which is 1 mm narrower and up to .002" thinner than the desired spring. A mainspring which is too long can be shortened, but be cautious about accepting a spring which is too short. I might replace a 90" mainspring with one that is 88" long, but differences of several inches may have an important effect on the number of barrel turns produced by the spring. This translates directly to run time and cannot be ignored.

To make the mainspring selection process easier, it would be useful to have formulas that determine exactly how many turns a barrel will receive from a given thickness and length of mainspring. The formulas I have tried are not consistent in their results and provide only an estimate. I suspect that differences in mainspring steel and barrel design are responsible for differences between predicted and actual performance.

Replacing a Barrel Hook

Barrel hooks cause a considerable amount of trouble for the repairer. In some clocks, especially 19th and 20th century German clocks, the hook is

Fig. 29. A tab that is stamped inward from the barrel wall is sometimes used as a barrel hook.

just a tab stamped inward from the barrel wall. Figure 29 shows this type of barrel, which often develops cracks around the tab. At other times a mainspring will break, and the force will flatten the tab against the barrel wall, ruining it. The only remedy for this inferior kind of barrel hook is to remove or smooth it flat and install a steel rivet halfway around the barrel from the point of injury. The making of a new rivet-type barrel hook will be covered in this section.

Fig. 30. This Urgos barrel has a steel rivet as a barrel hook. This style is better than a tab (Fig. 29).

Although the steel rivet is a better and more common type of hook than the tab-style hook, it also needs to be replaced on occasion. Figure 30 shows a rivet in a modern Urgos spring barrel. When this kind of riveted barrel hook has become loose, it is sometimes very difficult to tighten it again by re-riveting the steel hook tightly into the barrel wall. Figure 31 shows what frequently happens: the force of the coiled mainspring pushes out on the rivet, creating a loose rivet and a bulge in the barrel wall. This shortens the effective length of the hook that catches the end of the mainspring inside the barrel. It is necessary to flatten out this bulge as you

Fig. 31. This rivet-type barrel hook has been pushed out by the mainspring, creating a bulge in the barrel wall. It is difficult to tighten this hook again.

try to tighten the hook. Place the barrel over a large, round piece of steel held in the vise. The steel should have a hole or slot, and the rivet should fit into it without bottoming out. Use a small hammer, with a flat punch if you like, to flatten out the bulge and tighten the rivet, taking great care not to damage the barrel teeth.

When tightening a barrel rivet doesn't produce a trustworthy hook that you feel confident will stay tight, you should make a new hook to replace the old one. Considering the damage that can be done when a mainspring slips off a loose barrel hook, it is a worthwhile repair.

The first step is to drill out the old rivet in the drill press or on a miniature lathe with a vertical drilling attachment. It is better to drill a new hole on the opposite side of the barrel rather than trying to use the old, distorted hole for the new rivet. The

Fig. 32. Center drilling the hole for the replacement barrel rivet. A Sherline milling machine is used here.

new hole should be radial to the barrel and located in the center of the width of the space for the mainspring. A good way to drill the new hole is to use a small milling machine or a miniature lathe with a vertical drilling column set up as shown in Figure 32, with the barrel held in the machine vise. The handwheels can be used to place the center drill over the old hole as a guide; the barrel can then be turned about 180° around in the vise and retightened. The cross slide or "y" handwheel can then be used to move the vise as needed to establish a radial path for the drill (pointing to the center of the barrel). This can be done by measuring the way a machinist would do it, but I have found it works just as well to judge by eye when the hole will be radial. Center drill, then use a twist drill slightly

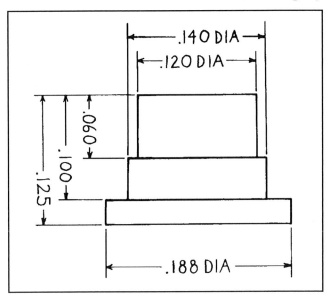

Fig. 33. This is a typical barrel hook with the dimensions shown in inches. The material is drill rod (steel).

smaller than the finished size, followed by the final drill (in this case a #31) to make the hole for the new rivet. Remove the barrel from the machine vise and use a hand-held countersink or counterbore to remove the burr from the inner and outer surfaces of the barrel at the hole location.

Figure 33 shows dimensions for a typical steel rivet for a chime clock. The dimensions can be changed to match the original rivet or make an improvement upon it, but at least the drawing gives a starting point. To make the rivet, a piece of 3/16" diameter drill rod (steel) is placed in the 3-jaw chuck of the miniature lathe. The smallest diameter of the rivet is turned first, and the finished piece is finally parted off the stock. The rivet is not heat treated.

At this point the remaining tasks are to insert the hook into the barrel wall, rivet it securely in place, and then finish the riveted portion flush with the barrel wall. These steps will determine how

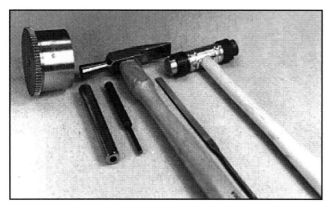

Fig. 34. Tools for installing a rivet in a mainspring barrel.

strong the rivet will be as a barrel hook and whether it will look like a professional repair.

Begin by selecting a piece of round steel stock at least one inch in diameter but preferably closer to the inner diameter of the barrel. Fasten the round stock horizontally in a bench vise with the end of the stock extending outward. An anvil may be used instead. Place the rivet inside the barrel and set the small diameter squarely in the edge of the hole in the barrel wall. A chamfer on the hole should allow the rivet to enter far enough to remain in place. Slide the barrel over the round stock and rest the head of the rivet against it.

Tools such as those shown in Figure 34 will be useful for the task. Use a hammer and a hollow punch to tap the barrel wall around the outside of the barrel rivet. This will force the rivet through the barrel and cause it to extend outside the barrel wall. Check to be sure that the rivet is seated. With the barrel still resting over the round stock, expand the rivet slightly by striking it with a riveting hammer (center in Figure 34) or a hammer and flat punch.

If the rivet diameter and the new hole in the barrel are the same, the new barrel hook will be a tight force fit in the barrel even before it is riveted. For this reason it should not be necessary to hit the end of the rivet with such force that the steel is

Fig. 35. The barrel can be polished in the lathe.

greatly distorted. To use excessive force is to increase the risk that you will miss with the hammer and dent the barrel. Deep marks cannot be removed, and they will damage the job at least from a cosmetic standpoint.

Although the new barrel hook is fully functional at this point, some further steps will do much to improve the appearance of the work. Carefully file the end of the rivet until it is flush with the O.D. of the barrel. Avoid making file marks in the barrel. To hold the barrel for filing, you can set it up again in the machine vise used earlier for the drilling. Once the end of the rivet is filed flush, polish the barrel with 280-grit paper. Move to finer abrasives such as a Scotch-Brite pad followed by 600-grit paper. This will leave the end of the rivet just a gray circle polished as part of the barrel wall. Hold the barrel in any way that is convenient. The polishing may also be done in the lathe as shown in Figure 35. An optional last step is to lacquer the barrel.

Loop-End Mainsprings in the Winder

By the end of Chapter 2 we had a loop-end mainspring held in a wire retainer or partially let down within the movement plates. The only safe way to completely let down and remove the mainspring is

Fig. 36. A loop-end mainspring and main wheel on a Keystone winder. The loop end of the spring is held on the steel post shown beneath the wheel.

to use a mainspring winder. Figure 36 shows an American main wheel and loop-end spring set up in a Keystone mainspring winder. Instead of using the rubber-lined clamp intended for barreled springs, the tool has an upright post with another post inserted at a right angle. This arrangement safely captures the loop end of the spring. Tighten the chuck on the winding square and turn the handle in the winding direction. It is not necessary,

Fig. 37. The larger view shows a mainspring in the author's Keystone mainspring winder, in a mostly let-down condition. When the spring is wound up (see inset) a wire retainer can be removed or installed from the spring.

at least with the Keystone mainspring winder in my shop, to constantly keep one hand near the mainspring or the main wheel. However, my Keystone winder was not manufactured with a ratchet on the handle for winding or unwinding. *If the handle "gets away" from the operator's hand, it will move very fast and may cause hand or other injury.* Wind until the mainspring diameter becomes small enough to allow the wire retainer to be removed (Figure 37, inset). Now carefully use the handle to allow the mainspring to slowly and completely unwind. *This description is for general background on a mainspring winder. It is not a user manual for the Keystone or any other mainspring winder. Always wear heavy gloves and eye protection when working with mainsprings, with or without a mainspring winder.*

Tightening the Main Wheel and Click

To gain complete access to the American click and ratchet wheel used with a loop-end mainspring, pry the inner end of the spring from the hook on the winding arbor and remove the spring. Set it aside for cleaning or replacement. Turn your attention to the main wheel.

Sometimes the main wheel is found to be loose on the winding arbor. The arbor must be free to rotate as the mainspring is wound, but the wheel

should not wobble. Figure 38 shows the slightly conical tension washer which holds the main wheel against the back of the click wheel. Tighten the washer by using a hammer and flat punch to strike the riveting which is already there on the hub of the click wheel. There are usually four points around the arbor where the riveting can be

Fig. 38. Use a flat punch to tighten the tension washer which presses the main wheel against the click wheel.

tightened. When you are finished, the winding arbor should still turn freely.

It is common to find that the click has become loose. Place the main wheel on an anvil so that the flat head of the rivet is facing down. Before striking the end of the rivet to tighten it, insert a thin shim under the click, as shown in Figure 39. This prevents seizing of the click. Most American click rivets

Fig. 39. Place a .004" thick shim under the click before tightening the rivet. This keeps the click free on the rivet.

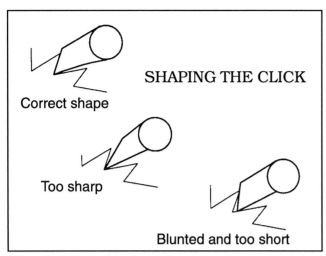

Fig. 40. Be careful when "cleaning up" a worn click by filing it. The click must fit the ratchet wheel to be safe.

are brass. Be extra careful when tightening steel rivets in any type of wheel; they tend to split if they are hit too hard.

Repairing a Brass Click

The clicks on American clock wheels with loop-end mainsprings become worn over the years from so much winding and an occasional "accident" from a breaking spring or a botched repair. Some of the clicks, like the Sessions example shown on the previous page in Figures 37 and 38, respond well to being "cleaned up" with a file. Remove the mainspring from the wheel, unhook the click spring, and move the click away from the ratchet wheel. It is a bit awkward to reach all the burred-over areas of the click, but it can be done. It is important to avoid changing the correct shape of the click—it may no longer fit the ratchet wheel.

Figure 40 shows a correct shape of a click at the top of the illustration. The click matches the shape of the ratchet teeth. If the click is filed to a sharper point as in the middle drawing, it will be weakened and very dependent upon the click spring. A click spring should bring the click into contact with the ratchet teeth; it should not be required to hold it in place. In other words, a good click would work by gravity alone if the wheel was oriented with the click on top of the ratchet wheel. The bottom sketch in Figure 40 shows what happens when a click is shortened and made stubby in an attempt to remove worn areas. The click does not fit the wheel and is no longer safe. A strong mainspring could pry this click up and over the ratchet teeth, causing a disaster.

Making an American Style Brass Click

When a click sometimes wears out or is damaged to the point that it no longer fits the ratchet wheel, it must be replaced with a new one. Assort-

ments of right and left-handed clicks are sold by supply houses, but it is difficult to find a piece in an assortment that fits a particular clock. It is better to take the time to make a replacement click than to spend an equal amount of time fussing over a "compromise" click that does not fit well.

Figure 41 is a sketch of a Forestville click that is a typical American style. Brass sheet of 1/16" (.0625") thickness is correct for duplicating most American clicks. The old click can sometimes be used as a pattern which can be traced on the sheet of brass coated with layout dye. Drill the rivet hole in the click first, clamping the piece firmly before drilling. Even small twist drills can catch in the soft brass and whip the piece around on the spinning drill. Keep your hands clear when using the drill press or any kind of drill, and always follow safe shop practices. Use a jeweler's saw to cut out the shape. Stay as close as possible to the scribed line to minimize the filing which will be needed to finish the click. Check the fit of the ratchet by placing it over the old rivet hole. Use a fine file to produce a slot in the top of the click for the click spring to rest in. In the other common style of American click, the end of the click spring was riveted into a channel filed into the underside of the click. This is more difficult to duplicate, but it can be done. Use the old click spring if it is still in good condition. If a

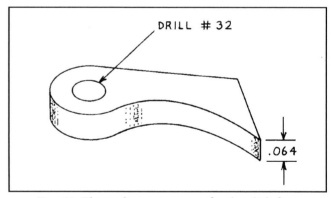

Fig. 41. These dimensions are for the click for a Forestville movement and are typical of American clicks.

new click spring is required, make it from brass spring wire. Try 18 ga. (.048" diameter) wire to start.

Make a new click rivet to go along with your new click. By doing this you can specify drill and hole sizes and control all aspects of the job. I usually drill out the original rivet hole in the main wheel to make a clean hole for the new rivet. The rivet should be about .003" smaller in diameter than the portion of the click that it passes through it. Many old clocks had rivets with just two diameters, the head and the shaft. I prefer to make them with three diameters, as shown in Figure 42. This makes a strong rivet. Brass is perfectly all right for American click rivets if the rivet is made well. Steel can also be used.

Figure 42 is a drawing of the click rivet that fits the click in Figure 41. The length of .062" for the smallest portion of the rivet was selected to pass all the way through this or any other typical American main wheel less than .060" thick. The extra material is used for riveting purposes.

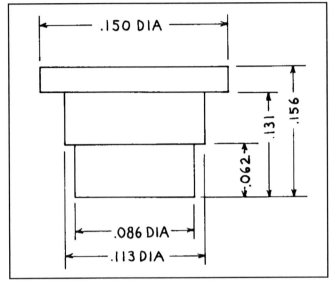

Fig. 42. Typical brass click rivet for an American movement. This one was for the Forestville movement.

Install the new rivet and click on the main wheel. First, cut the sharp edge off the small end of the rivet so it will enter the hole in the main wheel. Pass the rivet through the click and into the hole. Place the wheel flat on an anvil and use a hammer and flat punch to tap the rivet through the wheel. It is necessary to position the rivet over a hole in the anvil so that it can pass completely through. The rivet will not seize the click to the main wheel if the click is about .005" less in thickness than the length of the portion of the rivet which goes through it.

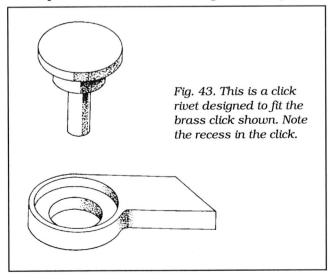

Fig. 43. This is a click rivet designed to fit the brass click shown. Note the recess in the click.

Turn the wheel over and place the head of the rivet on the anvil. Use the hammer and flat punch to spread the end of the rivet. Some force is needed, but do not destroy the rivet with heavy hits. If the rivet is a close fit in the wheel, very little effort is required to rivet it in place. Some repairers use a pointed punch instead of a flat punch. The end of the rivet should be nearly flush with the underside of the wheel. If it extends out too much, the rivet may interfere with the mainspring.

Figure 43 shows a click with a recess where the rivet fits into it. A new rivet is designed with the head fitting into the recess and ending almost flush with the surface of the click. It is easy to see why custom made clicks and rivets are better than those found in assortments. They fit much better and are a source of pride for the repairer.

Mainspring "Boxes"

There is a type of mainspring power unit shown in Figure 44 that is a combination of the open mainspring and the barreled mainspring. Seth Thomas and a few other makers used what is usually referred to as a mainspring "box". Although they look like barrels, these boxes do not rotate with the gears. The mainsprings are hooked to the boxes, which serve to contain them as they unwind and expand. The main wheels function just like main wheels with loop-end mainsprings.

The boxes are fastened to a movement plate. In the Seth Thomas it is a removable lower front movement plate. In some movements the boxes are screwed to the plate and can be removed easily and placed on a mainspring winder. The mainspring boxes shown here are riveted to the movement plate

Fig. 44. The power unit from a Seth Thomas No. 124 chime movement has three mainspring "boxes" riveted to the movement plate.

and are much harder to handle.

There are still other problems. The winding arbors are mounted opposite the open ends of the mainspring boxes. In addition, the winder needs access to the open end of the mainspring box, but the main wheel is in the way. It is no wonder that so many repairers do not clean and inspect these mainsprings.

The solution turns out to be similar to one covering the "normal" mainspring barrel of the type described earlier in this chapter. The clock's arbor is set aside, and another arbor is used in its place. The makers of the Keystone winder make these plain arbors available, but for the Seth Thomas No. 124 a special arbor was made to fit the job exactly. Clockmaker Mark Meadows provided the arbor sketched in Figure 45. It is ideal because it is similar to the clock's own arbor, but without the main wheel attached. The rear pivot of this special arbor fits the rear hole in the mainspring box to act as a helpful support for the mainspring as the winder is used.

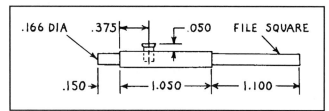

Fig. 45. Mark Meadows' winding arbor for use with Seth Thomas mainspring boxes and the Keystone winder.

Here is a procedure for removing the Seth Thomas No. 124 mainsprings for cleaning. It can also be used as a guide for working with similar springs in other movements. Let down the mainsprings first, using a let-down key. Remove the lower front movement plate which carries the mainspring boxes, mainsprings, and main wheels. If the boxes are held in place with screws, remove them to separate the boxes from the plate. If the boxes are riveted, they should not be removed. You can work around them.

Take off each main wheel by unhooking it from the inner eye of the mainspring. Just use a key to turn the winding arbor clockwise, opposite the direction of winding. These springs will unhook easily, without distorting the inner coil of the mainspring too much. Incidentally, unhooking mainsprings this way does not always work well with winding arbors and mainsprings from other clocks. It's a matter of how the hook is shaped.

Now you have three mainspring boxes containing coiled-up mainsprings. The winding arbor shown in Figure 45 is needed to temporarily replace the clock's own arbors, one at a time, as the mainspring winder is used. The mainspring box can be mounted in the winder like any barrel would be set up. It will

Fig. 46. The method for using the Keystone winder on riveted mainspring boxes is shown here.

probably be necessary to close the inner loop of the mainspring slightly with small pliers so the hook on the winding arbor will hold securely. Mr. Meadow's hook is made long enough to be effective, but not so long that it is difficult to remove later.

The riveted mainspring boxes are more difficult to handle. Figure 46 shows how they can be set up in the Keystone winder. The entire lower front movement plate is used as a lever to hold against the pressure of each mainspring as it is wound up. The springs are not so powerful that there is an unusual danger of the plate getting loose from your grip. Just be careful as you should always be when using a winder. Wear a heavy glove.

Slide a mainspring sleeve in place over the wound-up mainspring, then allow the mainspring to unwind within the sleeve. Unhook the outer end of the mainspring from the mainspring box, and remove the lower front movement plate from the winder. Finally, let down the mainspring completely, using the support post on the mainspring winder.

Stop-Works for Mainsprings

Our last topic under mainspring drives is the stop-works, sometimes called the Geneva stop-works. This setup is recognized as a pair of gears mounted outside the front plate; one is slipped over the winding arbor, and the other is usually held on a rivet. One gear has a shallow tooth-space, and the other one has a tooth longer than the others. When the long tooth and the shallow space come together, the arbor stops; this prevents the mainspring from being wound up all the way and also locks out the very lowest part of the mainspring's power. To set up a stop works, remove one of the two gears and then wind the mainspring fully. Then let down the spring one or two turns. Install the gear again and arrange the stop-works gears so they will jam if any further winding is attempted. Now let down the spring until the gears jam again. At this point there should still be enough power left to run the clock. Test run the clock for the full run time, usually eight days. If the clock is still running well past the seventh day and still has enough power to keep good time and strike reasonably fast, the stop-works is properly set up. If the clock runs down early, you need to rearrange the stop-works gears to permit the mainspring to be wound more fully before the gears stop the winding effort. That way there will be more power available at the end of the winding period.

You may run across a movement where the gear on the winding arbor is missing. This saved some repairer the trouble of setting up the mechanism. There is no harm in running the movement without stop-works, since most American movements did not have them anyway. To fully restore a movement, the missing gear would have to be made.

WEIGHTS

A weight is better than a mainspring for powering a clock. The weight provides a constant force from the beginning of the winding period to the end, and it does not lose strength or running time the way an ageing, dirty mainspring does. The main drawback of the weight is its lack of portability.

It follows that the greatest service problem with a weight is the breakage of the supporting cable or cord. Modern grandfather clocks have a special fault—the tendency for the weight shell to unscrew and fall apart. A weight suddenly cut loose for whatever reason may crash right through the bottom of the clock! Always check cables and cords when you repair a weight driven movement.

The Pulley
Many weight driven clocks make use of the pulley, a simple machine. Figure 47 is a diagram of two ways this simple machine may be used. The overall principle is that the mechanical advantage of a pulley is equal to the number of supporting strands. Let's say that by using a block and tackle (on the left in the illustration) a person wants to lift a heavy load; he or she exerts a pull for twice the distance of the actual lift, and in doing so halves the force required.

In a clock, as shown on the right in the illustration, this simple machine is operated the opposite way. As before, the mechanical advantage is equal to the number of supporting strands, which in the case of a clock is two. In the clock, the gear train is the load; the clock weight is the pull. This halves the distance over which the pull is exerted (the weight fall), but to do this a double-strength pull is needed. Fortunately, the winding arbor pivots must support only half this heavy pulling force, because the seatboard support carries the rest.

Any weight driven clock with a pulley arranged as shown on the right in the drawing is operating with a 2:1 mechanical "disadvantage". The diameter of the pulley does not matter. For the clockmaker, there are some practical considerations that

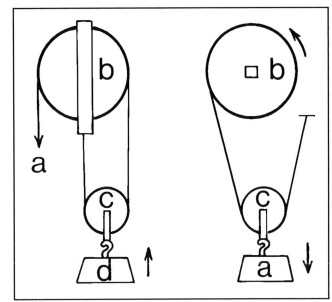

Fig. 47. A pulley as it is used in a block and tackle is shown on the left; the pulley as it is used in clocks is shown on the right. The parts are: **a** force; **b** fixed pulley; **c** movable pulley; and **d** resistance.

go beyond the principle of the simple machine. The pulley must be strong enough to withstand the load placed upon it and must have an undamaged groove large enough to carry the cable or cord. Check the pulley for wear, and clean it whenever the movement is cleaned. Oil the pulley because it will stop the clock if it becomes so stiff that the friction cuts too far into the power supplied by the weight.

Stop-Works on Weight Driven Clocks
A stop-works mechanism is considered by some to be an annoyance on a clock, especially a modern grandfather clock. Some of these same people have been known to remove the stop-works gears rather than learn how to install them. It really is not difficult to handle once the purpose and operation are understood.

The designer uses the stop-works in a weight driven clock to establish the upper and lower limits of weight travel. This can mean that the total weight fall can be set at 48 inches, for example. Beyond that, the stop-works is set up to prevent someone from over-winding the pulley into the seatboard. It also prevents the weight from descending to rest on the floor of the clock.

Like the spring driven stop-works covered earlier in this chapter, the stop-works mechanism in a weight driven clock uses two gears. A long tooth on one gear jams in a shallow tooth space in the other. One gear is removable and the other may be riveted to the front plate. In the weight driven clock, this mechanism halts the winding and later stops the weight fall.

Here is a general procedure for setting up the stop-works. Wind the weight until the pulley almost touches the seatboard, then mesh the stop-works gears so that the long tooth will jam in the narrow tooth space in the other gear as soon as the arbor is turned any further. Remove the weight, let out the cable, and confirm that the weight would have gone most of the way toward the bottom of the case. With the weight in the full "down" position, there should be at least a small amount of cable left on the drum.

Sometimes the set-up is a little more complicated than this. Three examples will help to prepare you for stop-works in modern grandfather clocks.

Hermle Flagship Series Stop-Works

In the Flagship movement, a gear is mounted on the winding square, on the left in Figure 48. This gear has 17 teeth, one of which is elongated. Meshing with this is a gear of 18 teeth, mounted on a post. This second gear has one tooth space which is shallow. When the long tooth and shallow space are brought almost into mesh, they will not pass, and at this point the gears lock.

If the gears are placed in the locked position and the click is released, it is possible to count the number of revolutions the winding drum will make. In this case the number is 18, less about 20° of one

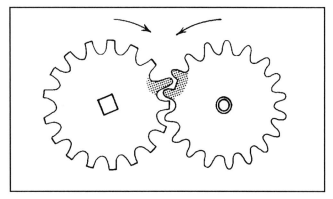

Fig. 48. Hermle Flagship Series stop-works. The gears turn inward as the clock is wound up; the teeth will not pass the shaded area.

turn because the teeth cannot mesh at the locking point.

The 17-tooth gear turns faster than the 18-tooth gear. If they are rotated away from the jamming point, after one revolution of the winding arbor, the 18-tooth wheel will be one tooth shy of having the jam occur. After two revolutions, it is two teeth back, and so on around the wheel. After 18 turns, the gears come around to lock again.

With a cable drum of 43.5 mm diameter, the circumference is 136.7 mm. The 18 turns will wind 2460 mm of cable off the drum. We need to deduct that 20° of one turn, however, so take about 8 mm off for a total of 2452 mm of cable. Since a pulley is used, divide this number in two to arrive at a weight fall of 1226 mm, or just over 48 inches. I tried this on a Flagship movement and measured a weight fall of 47-1/2 inches. As an estimate, the calculation checks out.

To set up the Hermle Flagship stop-works, wind the pulley up to a point just under the grandfather clock's dial or wooden bezel to establish the top limit. Note that Figure 48 shows the orientation of the Hermle strike stop-works with the winding arbor on the left. The mechanisms on the chime and time trains have the two wheels reversed. In our example, continue by slipping on the left-hand gear with the long tooth pointing just above a 3 o'clock orientation. Bring the other gear around with the shallow tooth-space just above a 9 o'clock position. With the gears set this way, you could not wind the clock any further. To check your result, you could let the cable out for almost 18 revolutions of the cable drum, until the stop-works locks at the lower extreme. This would show you how close to the bottom of the case the weight would come if the train were allowed to run out until it stopped.

Hermle 1161 Series Stop-Works

Repairers who attempt to set up a Hermle 1161 series grandfather clock have reported a problem. Although the weight was wound up to the desired height and the gears were set to jam at that point, the cable would only unwind a short distance before the clock stopped.

The problem is not with the stop-works. It is different from the Flagship series mechanism in that there are two shallow tooth spaces on the wheel instead of one. It is logical to ask why the wheel on the 1161 series movement has the additional shallow tooth space. The answer is that the second shallow space serves to reduce the total weight fall by one revolution of the cable drum.

To set up the 1161 series stop-works, wind the weight to the desired height. Arrange the stop-works gears as shown in Figure 49. If the key is turned

Fig. 49. Stop-works from a Hermle 1161 series grandfather clock movement.

further in the winding direction, the long tooth will jam in the *upper or clockwise oriented* shallow tooth space. The cable will unwind for a full run time.

Here's how it works. The 12-tooth gear on the winding arbor has the long tooth. The other gear, with the two shallow tooth spaces, has 13 teeth. As the clock runs, the 12-tooth gear turns counterclockwise; the 13-tooth gear turns clockwise. When the long tooth comes around one revolution, it now meshes with the 13-tooth gear at a point one tooth counterclockwise around the gear. Because the additional shallow space is there, the long tooth jams on the 12th time around instead of the 13th. If you set the stop-works initially using the wrong shallow tooth-space, the cable unwinds only one revolution of the cable drum before it jams.

Urgos UW66 Series Stop-Works

This section covers the stop-works on the Urgos UW66 movements made before 1994 (when the company was reorganized and set up to produce different movements). The UW66 stop-works operates on the same principle as the Hermle mechanisms described on the previous page. In the Urgos, however, there are fingers extending from the gear hubs instead of a long tooth and shallow tooth-space on the gears. The metal fingers butt together to stop the winding.

The Urgos mechanism shown in Figure 50 consists of two gears. There is a 24-tooth gear on the winding arbor with one metal finger. On a post next to the winding arbor there is a 25-tooth gear with two metal fingers. One finger stops the mechanism in the fully wound position; the other performs in the unwound position.

Here is a method for setting up the Urgos stop-works. Remove the 25-tooth gear from the post. Take off the weight temporarily so that you can wind up the cable, leaving about 6-1/2" of cable still extending below the bottom edge of the movement. Look for the reference mark on the face of each stop-works gear. Mesh the gears so that the mark on the 24-tooth gear points to 1 or 2 o'clock and the mark on the 25-tooth gear points to 7 or 8 o'clock. When the gears are set this way, any further attempt at winding should be prevented by the metal fingers on the hubs. Install the pulley and weight.

You can check the set-up by taking off the weight and pushing on the click spring at the back of the main wheel to release the click. Pull the cable out and verify that the drum turns between 17 and 18 times before the stop-works halts the action. Wind the cable up again carefully, checking for cable crossovers. Make sure the spring clips are in place to retain the stop-works gears.

Determining How Heavy a Weight to Use

There will be times when a clock comes in for repair and the weights are either missing or incorrect for the movement. If the clock is an identifiable type, finding the correct weight may be as easy as consulting a supplier's catalog. There you will find weights for one and eight-day cuckoo clocks, banjo clocks, Seth Thomas #2 regulators, bell strike grandfather clocks, Vienna regulators, OG clocks, and modern grandfather clocks. Suppliers listed in Chapter 1 will be able to sell these weights.

Problems come up when you know the type, such as a modern grandfather clock, but you still cannot determine the amount of weight required. There may not be a single correct answer for the weight. For example, a modern clock company in the U.S. purchased movements from Germany. The movement manufacturer gave its recommendation on the weight required, but the clock company made the final choice and purchased the weight inserts.

One way to determine the weight needed is to experiment. For a time train, install enough weight to barely run the clock. Then add another pound or

Fig. 50. Stop-works from an Urgos UW66 movement.

another 10% as you prefer. Test run the clock and make a decision. Excess weight will wear out the movement, and too little weight will cause the clock to stop frequently.

Extra weight will keep some worn or dirty clocks running for a brief period, but the clocks will stop soon enough. It is not a good repair procedure to knowingly add excess weight.

Sizing Cables and Chains

Cables come in various diameters. The correct cable should fit in the grooves in the cable drum. For drums that are not grooved, match the cable on the clock or ask your supplier's advice. Cable diameters range from 1/32" through 5/64" in brass, stainless steel, and braided nylon. Exact replacements are available for Hermle, Urgos, and Kieninger movements.

The length of a cable should be custom fitted to the movement and case. If the cable is too short, the run time will be reduced and the clock will stop with the weight hanging from the knotted end in the winding drum. This produces bad performance and invites a broken cable from the extra strain. A cable which is too long will bunch up and become crossed over on the cable drum. The result may be a clock that stops. A long cable may even foul the click, causing the weight to fall.

Chains can be a most difficult problem. If some links are stretched on a clock, these can be closed with pliers. If a chain is worn out or incorrect, try to order a replacement from a supplier. Unfortunately, the range of available links-per-foot sizes cannot possibly take into account every old clock in existence. Modifying or replacing a chain wheel to match an available chain is an option, but it is beyond the scope of this basic book.

The Endless Rope or Chain Drive

A special case of the weight drive is an old style movement which runs two gear trains from one weight. This causes confusion for the repairer who has not seen this drive method before. It is all the more confusing because there does not seem to be a way to wind one of the gear trains—there is no ratchet on the main wheel.

In this drive system, both gear trains take power from the same weight as they need it. One old London tall clock I repaired had the strike train on the left side, with the ratchet on its main wheel.

Various sources draw the set-up differently. Jesse Coleman, in *The Best of J.E. Coleman: Clockmaker* shows it as in my top sketch in Figure 51, where both main wheels turn inward. John Vernon, in *The Grandfather Clock Maintenance Manual*, describes the chain as in the bottom sketch, where both main

wheels turn counterclockwise.

To set a clock up correctly, first determine the direction of rotation of each main wheel. The ratchet orientation, plus the fact that the center arbor must turn clockwise, will certainly make this fairly easy to determine.

Next, picture one loop of chain draped over these sprockets, pulling them in the correct rotation. The pulley and weight are at the bottom of this loop.

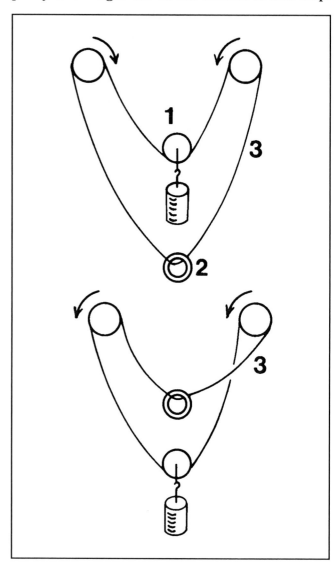

Fig. 51. *Two versions of the endless one-weight drive for a striking clock:* **1** *pulley;* **2** *lead ring;* **3** *winding location.*

The other loop passes through a small counterweight ring made of lead (available from suppliers). The chain or rope is joined and is continuous.

The relative sizes and positions of the two loops at any time will depend on whether the cord has been raised high or allowed to move down low. Wind the weight by pulling the chain or rope near the ratchet side.

4

PIVOTS & BUSHINGS

A beginning repair book is not the place, you might think, to read about pivot polishing and bushing work. If you do not have the use of a lathe, these topics are going to be filed under "future" in your personal course of study. For the time being, you want to be able to clean and repair some clocks.

There is a basic problem with that approach. It is just about impossible to work on clocks without some means of repairing the pivots—the axles on the end of each shaft, or arbor—and the bearing holes that support them. The pivots sometimes need to be finished to a slightly smaller diameter to remove grooves and then be polished. A worn bearing hole is properly repaired by the installation of a bushing. It is rare to find any clock that has been running for years and yet does not need pivot and bushing work.

The first step is to have the use of a basic lathe as described in Chapter 1. This will allow you to restore the surface finish on pivots. The second step is to learn to install bushings. Although bushing work can be done with inexpensive fixtures or even with hand tools, I think such methods should be considered temporary. Traditional "antique" methods for installing and finishing bushings can be learned, too, but for most of us a modern bushing tool is the answer. The use of the bushing tool will be covered in this chapter.

This chapter is about pivots and the way they fit into the pivot holes. It is essential to learn to recognize a hole which has been worn oval by its pivot, making it necessary to restore the pivot finish and then install a bushing in the hole. It is rare that every pivot hole in a movement needs a bushing; you must learn to distinguish between the worn holes that really need attention and unworn or slightly worn holes that are satisfactory.

PIVOTS

We will begin with pivots because they must be repaired and polished *before* any bushing work can be done. When the clock is apart on the bench, look at each pivot. You may be able to easily see an obvious defect such as a deep groove, but most repairers need an eye loupe to check for smaller defects such as a radius at the pivot shoulder. The fingernail test is recommended by Laurie Penman, the British clockmaker; simply slide your fingernail over a pivot and you will be able to detect roughness in the finish.

Figure 52 shows some of the common defects in pivots. The pivot at the top is a smooth cylinder, the ideal shape for most pivots. The end of the pivot may be slightly rounded for appearance, although it is not shown that way in the drawing.

The next view in Figure 52 represents a bent pivot. Pivots may become bent when a mainspring

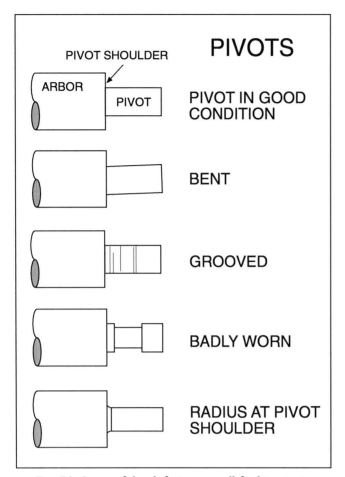

PIVOTS

PIVOT SHOULDER

ARBOR

PIVOT

PIVOT IN GOOD CONDITION

BENT

GROOVED

BADLY WORN

RADIUS AT PIVOT SHOULDER

Fig. 52. Some of the defects you will find in pivots.

Fig. 53. An arbor mounted in the watchmaker's lathe. Note the tool rest near the pivot to be repaired.

breaks or someone has an accident when trying to assemble or disassemble the movement. One way to straighten pivots up to about .060" in diameter (the size in most American clock movements) is to grip the pivot in a collet in the watchmakers lathe. Turn the spindle by hand, and when the arbor moves up to its highest point, push down on it. Try again until the arbor rotates without "running out". The pivot will then be straight. There is always a chance the pivot will break when it is being straightened. Be extra cautious with French pivots or any pivot that may have been hardened.

A grooved pivot, also represented in the drawing, is common. Install the arbor in the lathe and smooth it starting with a pivot file, then changing to a flat file and emery sticks. Follow up with several grades of finer polishing papers, up to a 100-grit paper. Grooves which are too deep may not be possible to completely remove without reducing the diameter of the pivot too much. If that is the case, polish the pivot as best you can. If the grooves are rounded by polishing, they may not affect the running of the pivot in its hole.

Wear sometimes takes the form of the pivot marked "badly worn" in the drawing. Replacement

of the pivot (repivoting) is necessary, since the diameter of the pivot would be too small if it were cut down to one smooth diameter along its entire length. The beginner is well advised to send the arbor, with wheel and pinion attached, to a specialist for repivoting. This comes up less often than one might expect, and many clock repair shops just send out the repivoting work to a specialist. It is not a basic clock repair topic for the beginner.

If a considerable amount of filing and polishing has taken place, a radius will develop at the pivot shoulder as shown in the bottom view in Figure 52. This radius should be removed so that it does not bind in your bushing and stop the clock. Install the arbor in a lathe fitted with a handrest, such as a

Fig. 54. A steady rest supports an arbor.

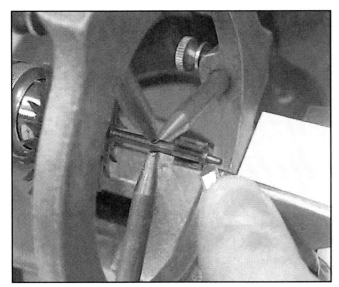

Fig. 55. Close-up of a graver being applied to a pivot.

watchmaker's lathe. Figure 53 shows this setup. A pivot file, available from suppliers, has a special profile which will cut into the radius. Another approach is to use a hand graver to restore a sharp corner between the pivot and the arbor. If your best effort still leaves a small radius at the pivot shoulder, you will have to use a countersink of the type found in bushing tool sets to slightly chamfer the replacement bushing. This slight chamfer is effective for all your bushings, even if there is no radius present at the pivot shoulder. The chamfer prevents binding of the pivot in the hole. It should not be used to compensate for a large radius, however. The pivot should be repaired.

Although the watchmaker's lathe is ideal for clock pivot refinishing work, sometimes a wheel or pinion is in the way, making it necessary to grip the arbor an inch or more away from the pivot to be polished. Without added support close to the pivot, the arbor will flex too much and will be impossible to work on. Most suppliers sell steady rests similar to the one shown in Figure 54 for watchmaker's lathes.

Figure 55 shows a graver being applied to a clock pivot. The sharpening and use of hand gravers is a subject unto itself. It is an ideal skill to develop in a class, where there is an instructor to show how the work is done. One of the most complete discussions of gravers is found in W.R. Smith's book *Clockmaking and Modelmaking Tools & Techniques.*

As an alternate, you may want to set the arbor up in a miniature lathe equipped with a cross slide. A light cut is made to equalize the diameter of the pivot throughout its length and to create a sharp corner at the pivot shoulder. It is not always easy to set up for this kind of pivot work in a miniature lathe. As with any lathe, you must be careful to

avoid extending the pivot you are working on too far out from the chuck. Even if your miniature lathe has a steady rest available, it may be difficult to fit it close enough to the headstock to support a clock arbor. W.R. Smith has pointed out that a skilled clockmaker can finish a pivot repair in the watchmaker's lathe using a hand graver in much less time than it takes just to set up a miniature lathe with a cross slide to do the same work. At least there is more than one way to accomplish the task.

Pivot repair and polishing can be described as the first step in repairing almost any clock movement. If no attention is given to the pivots, any bushings you install may not give good results. A rough pivot can wear out a new bushing in a very short time.

Bushings

Clocks have bearings which are nothing more than holes drilled in the brass plates. Steel pivots rotate in these holes. Unfortunately, grit embedded in the holes combines with dirt and clock oil to grind away at the walls of the holes. Pressure from the driving weights or mainsprings pushes each pivot against one side of its pivot hole, causing the hole to wear in an oval shape.

Most clocks need one or more bushings to form replacement bearing holes for the original holes in the plates. Some clocks need as many as twelve or

Fig. 56. A bushing is a brass sleeve which acts as a replacement for a worn pivot hole in the clock plate.

more bushings. This makes bushing work one of the main activities in clock repair. Some beginners try to ignore bushing work entirely, hoping their clocks will run after being cleaned and oiled. Others go to great lengths to devise methods of installing bushings with hand tools.

Two of the main concerns in bushing work are **1)** to center the hole before reaming it and **2)** to ream a vertical hole. Take care of these two points to assure that the correct distance between a gear and pinion will be restored and the bushing will be lined up with the opposite bushing or hole in the other clock plate. The best way to install bushings correctly is to use a bushing tool. Once the hole is re-centered, the tool assures that the hole will be

FIG. 57. HOW TO INSTALL A PRESS-FIT BUSHING.

PREPARE THE PIVOT HOLE FOR A BUSHING

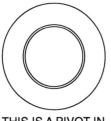
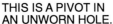
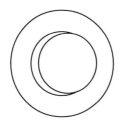
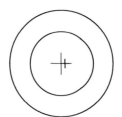
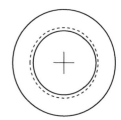

THIS IS A PIVOT IN
AN UNWORN HOLE.

NOW COMPARE A PIVOT
IN A **WORN** HOLE.

THE HOLE IS WORN
OVAL, SHIFTING THE
CENTER TO THE RIGHT

FILE THE HOLE UNTIL IT IS
ROUND AGAIN AND PLACED
ON THE ORIGINAL CENTER.

SELECT A BUSHING from an assortment. This is just a matter of picking out the one with the smallest bore that will fit over the pivot. Unless you have a huge selection of bushings, it will be necessary to enlarge the hole size later (see facing page).

INSTALL THE BUSHING

Once the worn pivot hole has been rounded out with a pointed file (see drawing above), it must be reamed out to accept the bushing. Reaming can be done by hand, but to obtain a hole perpendicular to the clock plate you should use a bushing tool.

Lay the clock plate on the bushing tool anvil and use the centering point (above) to center the plate under the spindle. Clamp the plate firmly. The Fitz-All bushing tool is shown.

Remove the centering point and install the correct size reamer for your bushing (top right photo). Ream the hole.

Use a "pusher" in the bushing tool spindle to tap the bushing into the reamed hole (right). The bushing is a friction fit and does not need riveting.

reamed perpendicular to the clock plate.

The drawing in Figure 57 shows that an unworn hole is round. In most cases, the hole is about .002" larger in diameter than the pivot, but in some clocks the difference in the diameters will be more or less than that. This means that you could compare the fit of an unworn pivot and hole in one clock to those in another clock and find that one was a looser fit than the other. Neither hole would need a bushing.

In contrast, a hole that is visibly oval might need a bushing. What standards apply when deciding which holes to bush? Beginners tend to either do no bushing work at all or to do unnecessary work on a number of holes that didn't need bushings. Some repairers have bushed *all* the holes in a clock, thinking that this will produce the best possible repair. The right approach is somewhere between the extremes. Instead of trying to apply some precise set of rules when deciding whether to install a bushing in each hole, I prefer to look at the movement as a whole. After getting the feel of the fit of a good pivot in a relatively unworn, round pivot hole in the clock, I compare this image to the other holes. It is not difficult to pick out the worst one or two holes, followed by some others that are oval and also need bushings. The rest of the holes in the clock are unworn or in relatively good shape.

You will also begin to recognize which holes are usually worn in certain types of clocks. The third strike arbor (front) pivot in an American clock and the second time train arbor (rear) in a French clock are examples.

Having decided to install a bushing in a pivot hole, you should use an eye loupe, if necessary, to determine which side of the hole is worn. Use a fine, round file to remove brass from the side of the hole opposite the wear. The drawing in Figure 57 shows how this moves the center back to its original location. You will know the hole is round again when it looks round from the front and the back side of the plate.

Select a bushing to fit the pivot. If you have a large selection of bushings, you may find one that fits like the pivots in the unworn holes of the clock. It is more likely that the best bushing you can find is too tight or may not fit on the pivot. This hole can be opened later with broaches.

Using the Bushing Tool

Install the clock plate in the bushing tool as shown in Figure 57. Follow the steps illustrated to ream the hole and install the bushing. Remember that each bushing system (KWM or Bergeon) uses reaming cutters that fit only the assorted bushings made for them. Bushings come in several lengths for different thicknesses of clock plate.

Fig. 58. A set of cutting and smoothing broaches mounted on a custom made bench stand. Included are two pin vises for holding broaches and two round files for rounding out worn pivot holes.

As explained earlier, it may be necessary to open the hole in the bushing with a broach. Clock broaches are sold in sets, with each broach tapered to fit a certain range of hole sizes (Figures 58 and 59). Fit the broach in a pin vise, a handle which allows you to insert the broach in the pivot hole and twirl it in your fingers. You must carefully maintain the broach in an upright position to avoid broaching the hole at an angle. One might ask: What

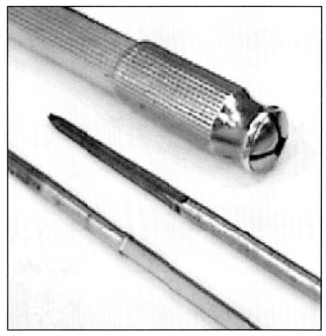

Fig. 59. Close-up of pin vise (top), smoothing broach (center), and five-sided cutting broach (bottom).

Fig. 60. The top bushing was installed with a bushing machine. The two bushings on the right received an added treatment—they were finished off with the cutters described on this page.

is the point of using a bushing tool to make upright holes, when a broach is used by hand to open up many of the bushings after they are installed? Broaching is a skill which comes with practice, giving you the ability to fit each bushing to fit the pivot just the way you want it. If you are finding it necessary to broach the bushings by a large amount, you probably do not have the right range of bushing sizes.

A smoothing broach, shown in Figure 59, can be used to finish the bore of a bushing after the reaming has been done. To complete the bushing, use the chamfering tool included with your bushing reamer set to take a light cut on the bushing hole at the inside of the clock plate. This removes any burr raised by the broaching and compensates for any slight radius found at the pivot shoulder.

Making Special Cutters for the Bushing Tool

The bushing method just outlined is based on the bushing tool, which is fast and accurate. Results can be improved, however, if the press-fit bushing is finished off to more closely match the clock plate. Two areas need to be modified: bushing length and oil sink shape.

With a few easy-to-make holders and inexpensive Dremel cutter bits, you can shorten bushings

Fig. 61. A press-fit bushing (left) has an improper oil sink, which should be reamed (right) to match the original.

to the exact thickness of the plate and recut the oil sinks to look more like the originals. The cutters fit into the bushing tool in the same way as reamers, and they do their work in a few seconds. There is little added setup time and no hand filing to be done. The modified press-fit bushing is hard to distinguish from the original pivot holes in the plate.

There is another benefit that goes beyond appearance. A typical bushing such as the KWM has a shallow oil sink which does not match the size or angle of most originals. When the oiler is applied to such a bushing, oil often runs over the top, filling the remaining part of the original oil sink, where it cannot lubricate the pivot. Figure 61 shows cutaway views of the bushings.

Steel cutter holders are easy to make for the Keystone bushing tool, and the idea should not be difficult to adapt to any bushing tool. A miniature lathe such as the Unimat or Sherline is ideal for this small project which involves turning, center drilling, and milling or filing a flat for seating a set screw. I have used these cutters for years with my bushing tool.

The material for the cutter holders is 3/8" diameter drill rod. Cut off about one inch of rod and mount it in the 3-jaw chuck. Face off the end. Turn

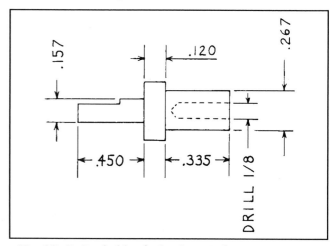

Fig. 62. Cutter holder for bushing tool using KWM-size reamers. This example was made for a Keystone tool.

the section to .157" as shown in the drawing, Figure 62. This is the diameter which fits into the bushing tool spindle for the KWM size. Remove the piece from the chuck and turn it around to be mounted in a #42 watchmaker's collet. Face the end, then turn the .355" diameter portion up to the shoulder, which remains at 3/8" diameter.

Center drill or locate the center with a graver. Drill the hole slightly smaller than 1/8" diameter, then finish with a 1/8" drill. The depth of the hole depends on the overall length of the cutter and holder which will be best for your bushing tool.

After drilling, polish the piece as desired. File the

flat for the set screw onto the .157" diameter portion. The cutter holder is now complete.

The Dremel tool bit shank must be shortened for use in the Keystone bushing tool. In considering how much to cut off for use in your bushing tool, keep in mind the depth of the hole already drilled in the cutter holder. Heat the tool bit shank to soften the steel, taking care not to affect the cutting end, then cut off the amount you need to remove.

The Dremel cutters have 1/8" nominal diameter shanks which I measured to be .1225". Use Loctite adhesive to fasten the shank in the 1/8" hole in the cutter holder. After the adhesive cures, install the completed cutter in the bushing tool. If the holder has been accurately turned and drilled, the cutter will not wobble as you turn the bushing tool spindle.

Using the Special Cutters

Figure 63 shows close-up views of the completed bushing cutters. Using these cutters adds some time to the bushing process described earlier in this chapter, but the end result is worth it. We will assume that the new bushing is slightly longer than the thickness of the clock plate and that the oil sink does not match the plate.

Fig. 63. Closeup of the bushing cutters made with Dremel tool bits and custom made cutter holders. The end cutter (left) is made from a Dremel No. 196 cutter, and the oil sink cutter (right) is based on a No. 100 bit.

There are some changes in how the bushing is installed. First round out the worn hole as described earlier. Then put the clock plate on the bushing tool with the outside surface facing *up*. Insert the pointed centering bit in the spindle and bring it down into the pivot hole as before, centering the spindle in the hole. Ream the pivot hole with the bushing reamer. Use the chamfering tool to remove the burr from around the reamed hole.

Next, place the bushing over the hole with the oil sink facing *up*. Press in the bushing with the pusher until the bushing is flush with the outside of the clock plate.

Without removing the clock plate from the bushing tool, remove the pusher from the spindle and

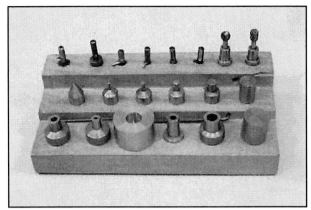

Fig. 64. The author's bushing tool accessory set includes the items from the Keystone set, plus a larger, custom made brass anvil (bottom center); and the two bushing cutters described in this section (top right).

insert the special oil sink cutter. Now cut the oil sink until it blends in with the clock plate, matching the original oil sinks in the movement. Usually the finish has chatter marks which must be removed. Light cuts, including some cuts made with an opposite rotation of the spindle, will smooth out the finish considerably. The resulting finish should be acceptable, but a better finish can be obtained if a tiny square of fine emery polishing paper is wrapped over the ball end of the cutter and used to polish the oil sink. Before reassembling the clock, be sure to reclean any movement polished this way.

At this stage the bushing is flush with the plate, and it has a matching oil sink. The plate should now be removed from the bushing tool, turned over, and placed back on the bushing tool anvil. The inside surface of the clock plate now faces up.

Use the centering bit to locate the bushing center, then clamp the plate firmly with both clamps. Next install the end cutter in the bushing tool spindle. Turn the spindle to cut the bushing until it is flush with the inside of the plate. Allow the cutter to take a light polishing cut on the inside of the plate, but no more. This polished circle is on the inside of the plate and will not harm the appearance of the clock.

In those cases where the replacement bushing is just the right length for the clock plate, the end cutter will not be needed. The process can be further simplified by installing the bushing the "normal" way first described in this chapter. That is, the bushing is pushed in from the inside surface of the plate. Then it is turned over for the finishing of the oil sink.

Figure 64 shows a bushing accessory set made up of the centering point, chamfering tool, reamers, pushers, anvils, and the special bushing cutters.

5

ESCAPEMENTS

Escapement work is one of the most fascinating aspects of clock repair, but it is also one of the most difficult to master. It is appropriate for the beginner, who is just learning to disassemble and clean clocks, to learn to distinguish the two main types of escapements and make basic repairs and adjustments. This knowledge will enable the repairer to correct many escapement problems. There will be times, however, when escapements require more experience to repair.

Although there are a number of different escapement designs in existence, the beginning repairer is most likely to encounter a group of escapements which are either of the recoil (anchor) type or the deadbeat type. In this chapter we will cover these main types including more than one example of each.

First, a few definitions will help. The *escapement* is the group of parts in the movement which measures out time. There is an escape wheel, generally a sharp-toothed brass wheel of distinctive shape, found at the opposite end of the gear train from the weight or spring which powers the movement. The *pallet unit*, also called the pallets or (in American terminology) the verge, interacts with the escape wheel to allow one tooth at a time to "escape", producing the ticking sound of the clock. A *suspension unit* of some kind is required as a support for the swinging *pendulum*, which establishes the speed at which the mechanism functions. In other words, the power unit drives the mechanism, the pendulum regulates it, and the escapement allows the mechanism to move ahead in definite steps. A

shorter pendulum will regulate a clock to run faster, but it still ticks ahead one escape wheel tooth at a time.

Recoil Strip Pallet Escapement

The recoil escapement was invented before 1660 and takes its name from the fact that the escape wheel backs up slightly at each beat. One recoil type, the recoil strip pallet escapement, was built into millions of mass-produced American clocks in the 19th and 20th centuries. It is a good escapement for beginners to start on because the pallet unit can be adjusted easily and can usually be replaced if

Fig. 65. A strip pallet recoil escapement of the front-mounted type is shown with a piece of white paper inserted behind the escape wheel for clarity.

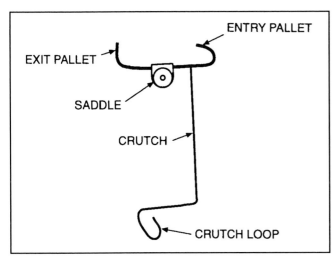

Fig. 66. Parts of the recoil strip pallet unit.

necessary with a new unit. Even the escape wheels are available for many old American clocks. It is a good idea to learn on clocks of a plentiful type, often of relatively low value, for which at least some parts are available.

Figure 65 shows a front-mounted escapement of the recoil strip pallet type. Other recoil strip pallet units are mounted between the movement plates and are adjusted and repaired in the same way. Figure 66 identifies the main parts of a strip pallet unit.

The following method of adjusting the strip pallet escapement is based on accepted ideas, notably the pallet closing procedure James Tigner described in AWI's *Questions & Answers of and for the Clockmaking Profession.*

Another definition is required before we proceed. *Drop* is the free motion of the escape wheel which occurs as one tooth is released by a pallet and another tooth is stopped by the other pallet. Most writers measure drop as the distance a tooth has moved following its release from a pallet. When the release has occurred from the entry pallet, it is entry drop (or inside drop); when it has occurred from the exit pallet, it is exit drop (or outside drop).

However, there is another way to measure drop explained in "The Square Recoil Escapement" (NAWCC *Bulletin*, April 1975, Whole Number 175, pages 149-180). Author Guy Aydlett defines this other way of looking at drop by stating that "drop can be visualized as *the airspace between the leading corner of a tooth-point and the part of the pallet it is about to fall on.*" Another well-known source, the English clockmaker John Wilding, also refers to escape wheel teeth dropping onto pallets in the escapement section of his book *The Construction of an Elegant Scroll Type Skeleton Clock.* I am more comfortable working with this second definition when adjusting a recoil strip pallet escapement, for

it is the drop of an escape wheel tooth *onto* a pallet which produces the ticking sound and the wear in an escapement. To accommodate all readers, both ways of describing drop are included in the steps which follow.

Adjusting the Recoil Strip Pallet Escapement

STEP 1: Repair the pallet faces. The pallet faces will almost always be found to have grooves worn into them by dirt embedded in the escape wheel teeth. Remove the grooves by filing or using emery sticks. If the steel faces are in a hardened condition, as they should be, it will be necessary to soften the steel first. Gripping the unit with tongs, hold a pallet face in a propane torch flame until the steel glows red. Slowly withdraw the pallet face from the flame and allow the metal to cool in the air. Repeat this with the other pallet face. Polish out the wear marks and obtain a bright finish on each pallet with fine abrasives. If the pivot holes for the escape arbor are worn, polish the pivots and install bushings before finishing this step. You cannot adjust a worn escapement.

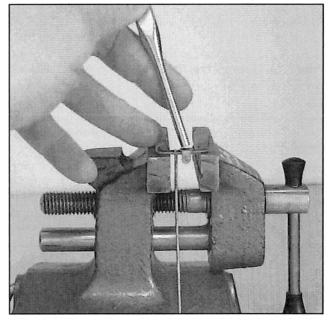

Fig. 67. Closing the pallets in Step 2 (Tigner's method).

STEP 2: Reduce the drop onto the straight exit pallet by closing the pallets. See Figure 67. Try the pallets in the movement to verify that the drop has been reduced.

For those who prefer this step stated another way: reduce the drop off the curved entry pallet by closing the pallet unit.

STEP 3: Reduce the drop onto the curved entry pallet.

Do this by reducing the center distance (the distance between the pallet unit and the escape wheel).

This is accomplished by moving the riveted cock which supports the pallet unit. Remove the pallet unit before attempting to move the cock. Pry or tap it according to the layout of the movement you are working on, but be careful not to damage any part of the movement. Some rivets are much tighter than others.

For those who prefer this step stated another way: reduce the drop off the straight exit pallet by reducing the center distance.

STEP 4: Harden the pallets. This is done by gripping the pallet unit with tongs and heating one pallet to a red color in the torch flame, then plunging it immediately into a container of water. This procedure will produce black scale which may be hard to polish off the steel. Some repairers coat the pallet with soap before heating it to prevent this formation. Others use powdered boric acid for the same purpose. To make the powder stick to the pallet, first heat the pallet very slightly in the flame. Then dip the hot pallet into the powder. Now proceed to heat the pallet to red and plunge it into water. The steel may take on a light gray color, but this is easy to polish off compared to black scale. Check the edge or corner of each pallet with an old file. If the steel is hard, the file will skate over the steel; but if the hardening process did not work, the file will cut the steel. Repeat the hardening procedure with the other pallet.

Installing Replacement Recoil Strip Pallets

Sometimes the strip pallet unit is so badly worn that it is a waste of time to try to refinish it. You can order a replacement strip pallet unit from a clock supplier. Unfortunately, the replacement unit will almost always need to be fitted and adjusted to work on your movement. This can be a time consuming process filled with frustration. The following section covers a procedure which simplifies the actions required to fit a new strip pallet unit to a clock.

STEP 1: Set up the escape wheel and old pallets with an escape tooth locked on the entry pallet as shown in Figure 68. Count the number of teeth spanned by the pallets. The answer will vary for different movements. The pallet unit shown in our example spans 7 teeth at entry lock.

STEP 2: Add 2 to the number of teeth from step 1. In our example, the answer will be 7 + 2 = 9.

STEP 3: Go to the escape wheel and dot any tooth as #1. Use a marker which can be cleaned off later. Count and then mark the tooth numbered the same as the answer in Step 2. For us, this is tooth #9.

STEP 4: Measure the distance across tooth #1 to tooth #9, from face to face, at the tip. It will be necessary to use an eye loupe and dial calipers. Figure 69 shows the idea. In our example, a Sessions es-

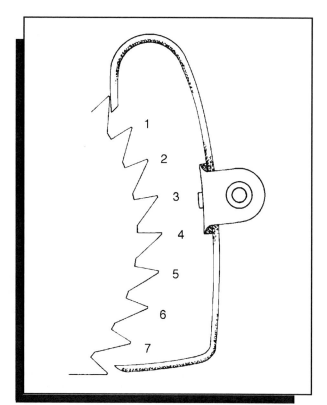

Fig. 68. Counting the teeth spanned at entry lock (Step 1 in the procedure for replacing a strip pallet unit).

capement, the measurement across the teeth is .777".

STEP 5: Subtract from the answer in step 4 the sum of one drop and one lock. The drawing in Figure 70 shows my interpretation of this concept, adapted from James Tigner's recoil escapement chapter in AWI's *Q & A* book. The amount of overlap, or lock, is at the entry pallet and the #1 tooth. The amount of drop (using the traditional defini-

Fig. 69. Measuring across the marked teeth (Step 4).

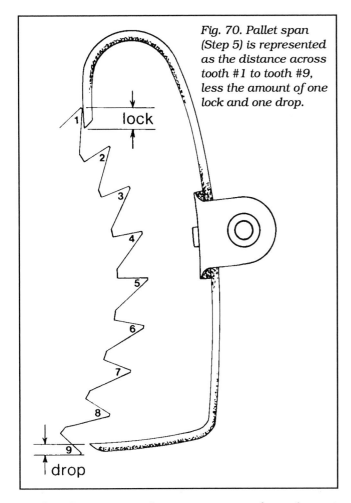

Fig. 70. Pallet span (Step 5) is represented as the distance across tooth #1 to tooth #9, less the amount of one lock and one drop.

tion) is the amount of movement away from the exit pallet for tooth #9.

Mr. Tigner suggests the combined drop-lock amount is 1.5 mm for most American recoil escapements, which converts to .059". Therefore, in our example the calculation is .777" - .059" = .718". This is the span which will be used for the pallets.

STEP 6: Now take your replacement pallet unit and make the span of the pallets (see Figure 71)

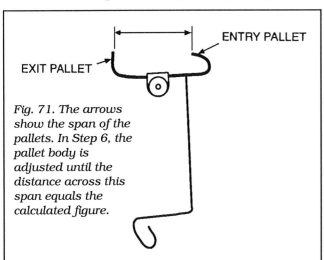

Fig. 71. The arrows show the span of the pallets. In Step 6, the pallet body is adjusted until the distance across this span equals the calculated figure.

equal to the span obtained in steps 1 through 5. This should give you a new pallet unit which is either correct or very close to correct. Above all, the new unit will probably function in the movement, unlike a raw replacement which might not allow escape wheel teeth to pass.

It is a great improvement to start your job of fitting the pallet unit if the span is within .002" to .010" of being correct—instead of an "as-is" replacement pallet unit that might be .080" off! Fine-tune the fit of the pallet unit with the procedure described under "Adjusting the Recoil Strip Pallet Escapement" beginning on page 37.

French Recoil Escapement

The pallet unit shown in Figure 72 is a recoil escapement, although it does not look much like the strip pallet units. The French pallet unit is a solid piece of steel with the pallets ground and polished in the locations shown in the drawing. The unit fits between the clock plates. There are only a few repairs which can be done on these pallets, since they cannot be reshaped like strip pallets.

The first step is to make sure the pivot holes for the escape wheel arbor and pallet arbor are in good condition along with the pivots. Next, observe the

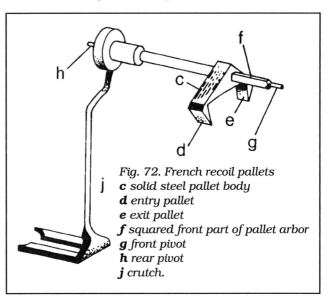

Fig. 72. French recoil pallets
c solid steel pallet body
d entry pallet
e exit pallet
f squared front part of pallet arbor
g front pivot
h rear pivot
j crutch.

escapement action. There is only one possible adjustment—raise or lower the pallet arbor pivot hole to change the center distance. This is accomplished by using a screwdriver to move the eccentric pivot hole for the front pallet arbor. Decreasing the center distance will reduce the drop onto the entry pallet.

If the pallet faces are scored or grooved, the marks can be polished out if they are not deep. If the wear is excessive, removing the grooves from the pallet faces will change the pallet unit so much that it will not function except with excessive drop. One adjustment that may help is to move the pallet body along the squared front portion of the arbor until a fresh area of the pallets is lined up with the escape wheel teeth. The pallet body can be cemented in the new location with Loctite.

English Recoil (Anchor) Escapement

Another type of recoil escapement is found in English bell strike and other movements. Figure 73 is a 19th century example. The entry pallet is on the left; note that it is straight compared to the

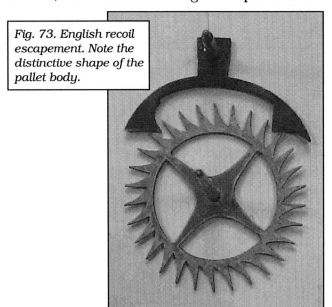

Fig. 73. English recoil escapement. Note the distinctive shape of the pallet body.

curved entry pallet on the American pallet unit. This escapement has a large amount of recoil which is easily seen by watching the second hand on the dial as it backs up after each tick of the escapement.

There is usually no means provided for adjustment of the center distance. You will encounter movements with filed-out pivot holes and other improper modifications to the back cock, which supports the rear pallet arbor pivot hole and the pendulum. The English pallet unit is likely to be in poor condition because of the age of the movement and the number of repairers who have worked on it. As with the French unit, some wear can be polished out, but the grooves are often too deep to be removed.

One way to repair a worn out pallet face is to replace it with a piece of thin, blue spring steel. File the pallet flat, removing a thickness of steel equal to the thickness of the spring steel. Soft solder the piece in place without using excessive heat which would soften the spring steel. If the steel surface comes to the exact height of the original pallet, the pallet may function normally.

If the pallet body has already been closed by squeezing in a vise, it may be so changed that starting over with a new pallet body will be necessary. Whether you begin with a piece of flat steel or a partially finished pallet blank from a supplier, this is an advanced clock repair task that the beginner usually cannot do without help.

Deadbeat Escapement

George Graham invented the deadbeat escapement in 1715, creating a significant advance in the accuracy of timekeeping. The name "deadbeat" comes from the fact that there is no recoil of the escape wheel following the lock onto a pallet.

The solid steel pallet unit is a precisely machined piece with hardened and polished pallet faces. Figure 74 shows the pallet center. From this center, two concentric arcs are drawn. A segment of the larger arc defines the entry pallet locking face; the smaller diameter arc on the opposite side defines the exit pallet locking face. In addition, two straight impulse faces, one entry and one exit, are cut at different angles.

Some deadbeat escapements allow one adjustment to be made. The center distance can be increased or decreased until the drops are equal. This adjustment is usually made by moving an eccentric pivot hole on the pallet arbor. Some other deadbeat escapements are not adjustable in any way, including the adjustment of center distance. Perhaps that is the reason so many deadbeat escapements are ruined by frustrated repairers who file the pallet faces or escape wheel teeth in an attempt to make the escapement work. One repair that does work is to re-bush worn pivot holes for the pallet and escape arbors to restore the correct center distance and reduce friction.

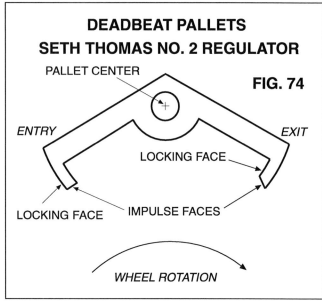

DEADBEAT PALLETS
SETH THOMAS NO. 2 REGULATOR
PALLET CENTER
FIG. 74
ENTRY   EXIT
LOCKING FACE
LOCKING FACE   IMPULSE FACES
WHEEL ROTATION

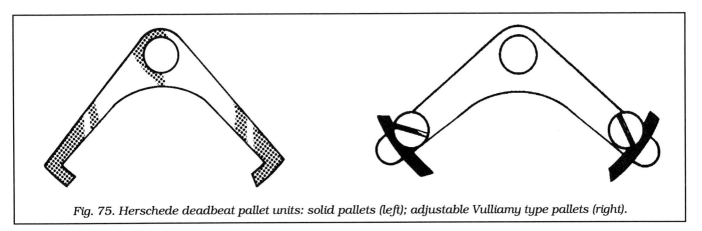

Fig. 75. Herschede deadbeat pallet units: solid pallets (left); adjustable Vulliamy type pallets (right).

There is a special style of deadbeat escapement, the Vulliamy, which allows adjustment of each pallet separately. Figure 75 compares this style to a standard deadbeat unit. In the Vulliamy, the brass pallet body has two grooves cut concentric with the pallet arbor. Into these grooves are fitted hardened, polished steel pallets, each held by a set screw. This means the pallets can be replaced if they are worn. In many movements, the replacement is done by removing the double-ended pallets and switching them, upside down, to the opposite side of the pallet body. Vulliamy pallets rarely need adjustment unless someone else has moved them out of place. Do not move the pallets except as a last resort, when you are sure they have been moved out of place.

The most common clocks with Vulliamy pallets are certain 400-day clocks. These clocks are usually inexpensive, making them ideal subjects for the beginner who would like to learn the adjustment of Vulliamy pallets. For a complete tabulation of deadbeat adjustments, read Terwilliger's *The Horolovar 400-Day Clock Repair Guide*, which contains an excellent escapement chapter by Henry B. Fried. The information is tabulated for Vulliamy pallets in an escapement which allows the adjustment of center distance.

Analyzing a Deadbeat Escapement

Here is a procedure the beginner can follow to determine whether some kind of repair is needed to a solid steel pallet unit. The underlying problem, as stated before, is that there is little or no adjustment possible in the majority of solid steel deadbeat pallet units.

STEP 1: Observe the escapement action by removing the pendulum and moving the crutch slowly from side to side. Some movements allow a good view of the escape wheel and pallets, but others are more difficult to see. Look for bent escape wheel teeth, then carefully watch the escape teeth fall onto the pallets to determine whether the teeth fall properly onto the locking faces.

STEP 2: Adjust the center distance if it is necessary. Your observation of the escapement may reveal that the escape wheel teeth actually *mislock* directly onto the impulse faces of the pallets. This destroys the deadbeat action and invites rapid wear if the clock continues to run this way. There is just one possible adjustment—the one which corrects the center distance. If there is an adjustable pallet arbor bushing, move the eccentric pivot hole to bring the pallet unit closer to the escape wheel, reducing the center distance. If there is no adjustment, check to see if the pivot holes are worn badly enough to cause excessive center distance. Install bushings and polish pivots as needed.

STEP 3: Check the pallet faces for wear. With some difficulty, slight grooves or scratches can be removed with emery sticks, and the pallets may be further polished to a bright finish. When polishing by hand, it is important to avoid rounding off the sharp corner between the locking and impulse faces. Further, it is very difficult to reach the locking face on the exit side (see Figure 74). As an alternative, especially when the damage is more severe, you may be able to move the pallet unit to bring a fresh section of the pallets to bear on the escape wheel teeth. It may not be possible to shift the pallet body if it is too thin or if there are other parts of the movement in the way.

If severe pallet wear has occurred, removing steel by filing and polishing may destroy any hope of returning deadbeat action to the pallets. Textbooks discuss various means of restoring lost metal to the pallet faces, including adding replacement tips of hardened steel and "closing" the pallet body. Adding steel can be difficult, especially on a small pallet unit. Closing the pallet body to bring the tips of the pallets closer together alters the correct shape, creating recoil or other problems.

At some point, if all adjustments and repairs have been tried without success, a decision must be made to fit new pallets to a movement. If the movement is a modern one such as a Hermle or Herschede unit, obtain a replacement pallet unit. It may be possible to obtain a pallet unit for other movements from a scrap movement of the same model as the one being repaired. A pallet unit for most other clocks would have to be made by a clockmaker. Pallet making is an advanced project.

The Brocot Escapement

The Brocot is a common escapement in French and American clocks made in the 19th and early 20th centuries. It is generally intended as a dead-beat form, although some examples have recoil at least on one side. The escapement is easily recognized by the D-shaped steel or jewel pallets set in a brass pallet body. The escape bridge and pallet body are often graceful, curved pieces that add to the appeal of the mechanism. Figure 76 shows the design, which is almost always arranged to be seen in the center portion of the dial. This "visible" escapement is fascinating to watch, but it has caused repairers much difficulty.

The escapement is often found to be damaged because the delicate escape teeth are bent, the pallets have been set incorrectly, or the pallet body has been distorted in an attempt to repair the clock. Always check the pivots and pivot holes of the escape arbor and pallet arbor. A movement with worn pivot holes in the escapement cannot be adjusted.

As shown in the drawing, the pallets are round pieces cut down to the diameter. Pallets are made of steel or red colored jewels. The steel pallets are subject to wear; the red-colored jewel pallets are more likely to be broken or lost. If the pallets are worn, missing, or the wrong size, they must be replaced. The size can be established by starting with the pitch, the distance between escape wheel teeth. Pitch can be measured with dial calipers if you use an eye loupe to improve your view. You can also calculate pitch: multiply the diameter of the wheel by π which is 3.1416; divide the result by the number of teeth on the wheel. The diameter of the new pallet should be 90% of the pitch value. This means the new pallet will just fit between the escape wheel teeth. A supplier may have just the size pallets you need in steel or jewel, but sometimes it is necessary to make new pallets from steel.

In some clocks, steel pallets are a friction fit in the pallet body. In others, steel or jewel pallets are held in place with shellac. Suppliers sell the shellac in flake form. When placed on the back of the pallet, a small flake will soften and flow around the pallet and into the hole when heat is applied to the

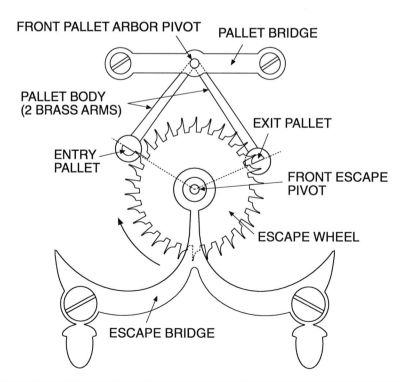

Fig. 76. Main parts of the Brocot escapement. The dotted lines radiating from the center of the escape wheel show the initial setting for the pallets. When the escapement is adjusted, it may be necessary to slightly twist one or both pallets to prevent the teeth from catching on the pallets.

BROCOT STYLE ESCAPEMENT
BASED ON AN ANSONIA MOVEMENT

FRONT PALLET ARBOR PIVOT   PALLET BRIDGE

PALLET BODY
(2 BRASS ARMS)

ENTRY
PALLET

EXIT PALLET

FRONT ESCAPE
PIVOT

ESCAPE WHEEL

ESCAPE BRIDGE

area. This cements the pallet in place. The best way to apply heat is with a small soldering iron fitted with a tip that has no solder on it. Do not use a torch. Once the shellac is warmed, the pallet can be moved for a few seconds before the shellac sets again. Solder, "Super Glue", and Loctite type adhesives should not be used on these pallets.

An initial setting is to point the flat of each pallet at the center of the escape wheel as shown in Figure 76. Sometimes it is necessary to further twist one or both pallets slightly to prevent the escape teeth from catching on the corners of the pallets.

There is often no adjustment on the center distance, although it is critical to the operation of the escapement. In the Ansonia escapement pictured in Figure 76, the escape bridge can be turned upside down or bent slightly with the fingers to change the center distance. If the center distance is too great, the entry pallet will catch on a tooth; if the distance is too small, the exit pallet will catch. Center distance is also adjusted to equalize drop at the two pallets, but in practice it seems that the depth has more to do with whether the escapement functions at all than whether the drops are exactly equal.

The other main adjustment is to try to correct a distortion of the pallet arms created by another repairer. The pallets can be closed to increase the amount of lock or opened to decrease it. The correct lock occurs when the tip of an escape tooth strikes the center of the rounded pallet. Too much lock causes extra drag over the pallet, requiring a wider swing; too little lock causes a jarring recoil as the tooth climbs the rounded pallet.

Consider the variables: the escape teeth may have been bent or shortened; the pallets may be an incorrect size or pointing at the wrong angle; the pallet bridge may be bent or reversed; and the pallet body may be distorted. All this adds up to a difficult task of repair and adjustment. As a method, consider the pallets and their angle first, a possible depth error second, and a possible distortion of the pallet body third. Avoid making changes to the center distance or pallet body unless you are certain they have been changed by someone before you.

Do not be concerned if some recoil remains in a properly adjusted Brocot escapement—it may not be a true deadbeat. As an example, an Ansonia movement was manufactured with a center distance almost 1/4" shorter than the distance required to eliminate recoil on the entry pallet.

Half-Deadbeat Strip Pallets

A minority of American clocks with short pendulums have an unusual strip pallet escapement called the half-deadbeat. It is a confusing mechanism for repairers because it looks so much like the com-

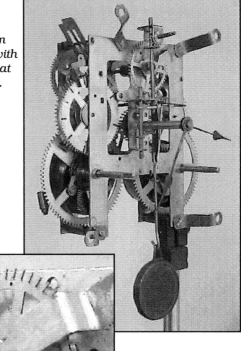

Fig. 77. The half-deadbeat, strip pallet escapement is found in some American movements made in the late 19th and early 20th centuries.

An Ingraham movement with half-deadbeat escapement.

The escape wheel and pallet unit.

mon recoil strip pallet escapement. For purposes of repair and adjustment, however, the half-deadbeat follows the rules of the deadbeat escapement.

Figure 77 shows a movement by Ingraham, which seems to have produced a large proportion of the movements with half-deadbeat escapements. The Ingraham escape wheel is a relatively large 1.5" in diameter and has 48 fine teeth. These movements were used in black mantel clocks and other small shelf clocks requiring a short pendulum of approximately 5-1/2". Gilbert and Seth Thomas also used this escapement in some gong strike floor clocks and mantel clocks.

The half-deadbeat escapement is a relative of the deadbeat, but the escape wheel teeth do not quite remain motionless or "dead" after they drop onto the pallets. This happens because the locking faces do not lie on arcs struck from the pallet center. That's where the term "half" comes into play, because the escapement is not truly deadbeat.

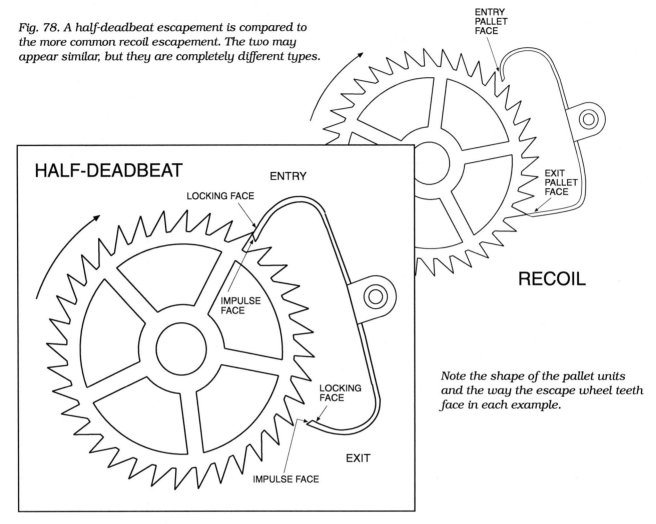

Fig. 78. A half-deadbeat escapement is compared to the more common recoil escapement. The two may appear similar, but they are completely different types.

HALF-DEADBEAT

ENTRY

LOCKING FACE

IMPULSE FACE

LOCKING FACE

IMPULSE FACE

EXIT

ENTRY PALLET FACE

EXIT PALLET FACE

RECOIL

Note the shape of the pallet units and the way the escape wheel teeth face in each example.

A comparison of the half-deadbeat and recoil escapements is shown in Figure 78. The half-deadbeat pallet unit has four faces, two locking and two impulse. Repairers are sometimes confused because it looks like the recoil strip pallet has these same four faces, but in fact it has only two faces. The angles cut onto those pallets are just for clearance of the escape wheel teeth.

At a quick glance, it is possible to distinguish the half-deadbeat strip pallet from the recoil. Just look at the shape of the pallet unit (symmetrical or not) and the direction the escape wheel teeth lean (toward the pallets or away from them).

Adjusting Half-Deadbeat Strip Pallets

Because of the fact that the pallets are the strip type and do not have the angles for the dead-locking of escape wheel teeth, it is possible to repair and adjust the pallets using methods that do not work with the true the true deadbeat. The reasoning is that the half-deadbeat strip pallets are bendable, which makes them easily adjustable. The adjustments will change the pallet angles, but one cannot

destroy a deadbeat action that was never there. The limit is reached when a half-deadbeat pallet is so worn that it cannot be adjusted to function again.

First of all, observe the escapement to check whether the teeth drop onto the locking faces as they should. The amount of overlap of the tooth on the pallet face is called "lock". The easiest adjustment to make is to move the pallet cock to change the center distance. If reducing the distance restores a normal lock, the adjustment may be complete. Always check the escape pivot holes for wear, since a worn escapement cannot be correctly adjusted. The escape wheel teeth should also be checked for bent tips. These can be carefully straightened with needle nose pliers or heavy tweezers.

Next, check the four pallet faces as you would in any deadbeat escapement. Even if the escapement is still functional, you may want to file and polish out any grooves from these pallet faces. As described earlier in this chapter under "Adjusting the Recoil Strip Pallet Escapement", it will be necessary to soften the steel pallet faces so they can be polished. Try to avoid rounding the edge between the locking face and impulse face of each pallet. It will be especially difficult to reach the locking face on the exit side. When the pallet faces are in good condition again, check the pallets in the movement.

At this stage you may find that the lock is reduced to zero or the teeth actually mislock directly onto the impulse faces. Correct this by closing the pallets using the method used on recoil pallets.

Try the pallets again in the clock. Make further adjustments to the center distance if necessary. If the escapement is in good condition, there will be a minimal but safe lock on all escape wheel teeth. In addition, there should be no chance that a tooth will jam on a pallet. The last step is to reharden the pallet faces and polish them a final time.

Fitting a Half-Deadbeat Strip Pallet Unit

A half-deadbeat pallet unit is sometimes distorted by a repair effort and will not operate. At other times the pallet unit must be replaced with a new one. Here is a three-step estimating method for establishing a *working distance* between the two pallets. Once the pallets will at least function, they can be adjusted as described in the previous section.

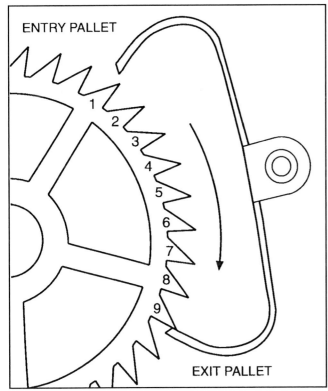

Fig. 79. Step 1 will establish the span of the pallets. Use the old pallets as a guide as shown above: lock the exit pallet on an escape tooth and count the number of teeth spanned by the pallets. In this Ingraham example, the number of teeth spanned is nine. Mark the first and last tooth spanned. In this case you would mark any tooth as #1 and then mark tooth #9. Use a marker which can be cleaned off later.

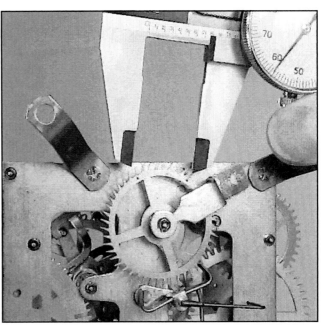

Fig. 80. Step 2 measures the distance across the number of teeth from Step 1. In our example the distance across nine teeth is .759". Dial calipers reading in thousandths of an inch (above) are required for the measurement.

Fig. 81. In Step 3, add the amount of .009" to .012" for the entry drop (the space between tooth #1 and the entry pallet) to the distance obtained in Step 2. The result is the estimated distance between the entry pallet let-off edge and the exit pallet locking face. In our example, the final value is .768". If a replacement pallet unit is set to that measurement, it will function in the clock. It can then be given final adjustments.

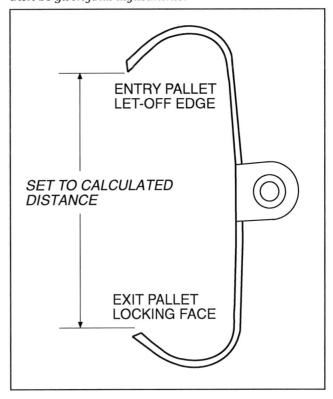

6

TIMEKEEPING

The need to regulate a clock is one of the first concerns of the new repairer. Whenever a clock is repaired, adjustments must be made to eliminate time gain or loss to the greatest extent possible. None of these efforts will create the perfect clock; timekeeping errors are built into escapements and are worsened by uneven power from mainsprings and other factors, including the drag caused by strike and chime mechanisms.

The two basic means of regulation are the *hairspring balance* and the *pendulum*. Both accomplish the same task by controlling the rate at which the escapement operates. The tools and knowledge to work on these mechanisms are very different. I will begin by explaining the reasons why the new repairer, especially one who is to be self-taught, would do well to steer clear of most balance-controlled clocks for a period of time, concentrating instead on pendulum clocks.

Figure 82 shows a platform, a detachable balance escapement made up of an escape wheel, balance wheel, hairspring, and pallets. The coiling and uncoiling of the hairspring performs the same function as a swinging pendulum. However, years of skill and practice are required to enable the clockmaker to straighten, adjust, and replace hairsprings. Older clocks with inexpensive balance escapements are often badly worn out and are unlikely to respond to any but the most expert attention. To make matters worse, clock hairsprings are difficult to find in

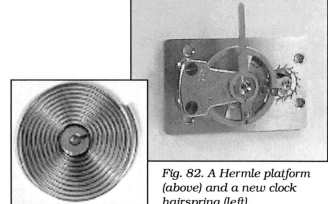

Fig. 82. A Hermle platform (above) and a new clock hairspring (left).

the correct sizes. (Fitting a new hairspring to a balance is a watchmaking skill called *vibrating*.) On the other end of the scale, the high-grade, jeweled balance escapements found in some clocks require even more of the watchmaker's skills and tools. The parts are small and extremely delicate, and hairsprings are just as hard to find for these balances. Everything about a high-grade balance unit—the fit and finish of the parts, the level of cleanliness required, and the method of oiling—serves to set it apart from most clock movements.

A special case of the balance escapement is the floating balance shown in Figure 83. This unit, with its helical hairspring, was originated after World War II by Hettich, a German company. For over 30 years, Hettich supplied floating balances to the clock industry. In particular, Hermle installed millions of

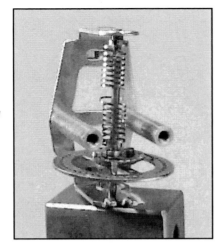

Fig. 83. A floating balance unit.

floating balances in mantel clock movements. When Hettich stopped manufacturing in the 1980's, Hermle began using a large balance wheel with a flat hairspring in place of the floating balance. Many of the clocks which came equipped with floating balances are out of service now. Repairers who work on Hermle movements can either replace the older floating balance units with the new balances or try to locate a supplier who still has the old floating balance units in stock. As Joseph Cerullo wrote in *Clockmakers Newsletter* in 1988: "The floating balance will go down in history as a short-lived oddity in horology." See the references at the end of this chapter for more reading on the subject.

The pendulum had its first application to clockwork in the drawings of Galileo's escapement, conceived shortly before his death in 1641. The pendulum is a swinging mass which unlocks the escapement with each swing. The period of the swing of the pendulum is based on its length. The accuracy of the pendulum is reduced from the theoretical because it operates in the air, not in a vacuum, and because temperature changes cause expansion and contraction of the materials of which the pendulum is made, changing its length. These changes cause variations in the clock's rate.

For the repairer, there are several practical pendulum skills required: how to regulate the length of a pendulum as efficiently as possible; how to calculate the number of beats per hour a particular clock should make; and how much to add or subtract from a pendulum unit if it is the wrong length.

Figure 85 shows the main parts of a pendulum. To regulate a pendulum clock, the pendulum bob

Fig. 84. A kitchen clock pendulum.

is raised to make the clock go faster and lowered to make the clock go slower. The rating screw has a rating nut threaded onto it, with the pendulum bob resting on the nut. It is important to make sure that the pendulum bob will descend when the screw is lowered. If the bob is too tight on the pendulum shaft, the bob does not descend. Sending a clock back to a customer this way is asking for trouble, since the owner may lower the nut but not achieve any noticeable slowing of the movement as a result. It is a common problem on modern grandfather clocks with the lyre pendulums made up of brass and steel rods instead of a single pendulum shaft. Find the source of the binding and try to relieve it without making the bob so loose that it wobbles on the shaft. In some pendulums there is a tab on the

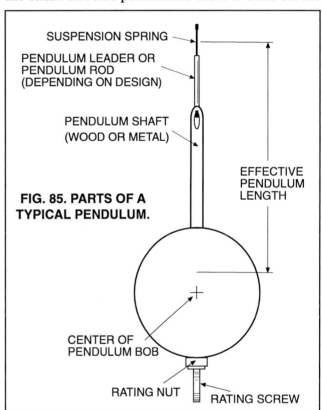

SUSPENSION SPRING

PENDULUM LEADER OR PENDULUM ROD (DEPENDING ON DESIGN)

PENDULUM SHAFT (WOOD OR METAL)

EFFECTIVE PENDULUM LENGTH

FIG. 85. PARTS OF A TYPICAL PENDULUM.

CENTER OF PENDULUM BOB

RATING NUT   RATING SCREW

back of the pendulum bob that can be bent slightly to eliminate the binding. Some modern pendulums have a rating nut with a washer built into it that fits into a slot in the bottom of the bob. This drags the bob downward when the screw is lowered, thereby assuring positive action.

If a clock is set up and then gains or loses time, it can be a long process to reset the hands and then raise or lower the bob by trial and error—you have to wait for hours, or perhaps a day or more, to check the time again and find the new error. A simple technique will save time. Let's say a clock is set up and shows a loss of ten minutes in one day. Rather than raise the pendulum bob a small amount, raise it a large amount instead. This could be an inch or all the way to the top of the adjustment, depending on the clock. Because the clock lost time initially, you need to make it gain to show whether it can be regulated. It would be a waste of time to keep raising the bob a small amount, reducing the loss slightly, then waiting, raising it again, and so on.

The suspension spring (see Figure 85) is the piece connecting the pendulum to its point of suspension in most clocks. The spring should be replaced if it is kinked or damaged in any way, since it can cause the pendulum to wobble. Most suspension springs are made up of top and bottom fittings with one or two pieces of spring steel between them. The length of the suspension spring affects the length of the pendulum, but more important than this is the effect of thickness, normally in the range of .003" to .006". Having the wrong thickness for a particular clock may cause it to stop or may influence the pendulum, placing the regulation outside the limits of the rating nut and screw.

Figure 85 shows that the effective length of a pendulum runs between the flexing portion of the suspension spring to a point usually somewhat above the actual center of the pendulum bob. This shift occurs because all the mass of a pendulum, even the material in the pendulum shaft and the rating nut and screw, affects the center of mass. Removing or adding material such as decorative brasswork to the pendulum assembly will change its effective length. This effective or theoretical length can be calculated based on the gearing in the movement, as explained in the next section. However, it is not possible to approach the problem from the opposite direction by looking at an existing pendulum and *precisely* measuring its effective length. An estimate is the best one can manage.

Beats Per Minute and Pendulum Length

Sometimes a pendulum cannot be adjusted to the correct rate or it is missing from the clock. Changing the length of the pendulum shaft or fitting a new pendulum by trial and error can mean cutting off numerous small amounts and perhaps shortening it too much. A better approach is to count the teeth on certain wheels and pinions when the movement is disassembled. A few calculations with these numbers will yield the number of beats per minute and the effective pendulum length in inches. Figure 86 shows the appearance of the typical clock wheel teeth and pinion leaves that must be counted.

The first step in determining beats per minute (BPM) is to count the teeth on the appropriate wheels and then multiply these counts together to form a number. (The practical examples on the next two pages will help you to select the wheels to include.)

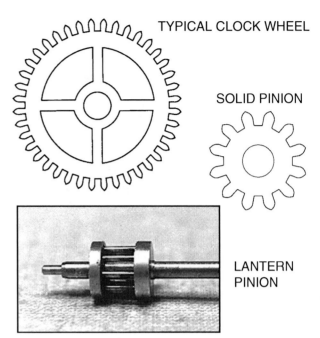

Fig. 86. Gear forms.

Certain pinions must also be identified, the leaves counted, and the counts multiplied together to form a number. The "wheel" number is placed over the "pinion" number as a fraction. This calculation is just a way of working with the individual gear ratios in the portion of the time train extending upward from the center arbor, which turns once per hour, to the escape wheel. After the fraction is reduced the result is multiplied by 2, since each escape wheel tooth is touched by each of two pallets. The number obtained is the beats per hour (BPH) which is needed if you are going to use a modern electronic clock timer. Divide the BPH by 60 to obtain beats per minute (BPM). The BPM is then used in calculating the effective length of the pendulum.

There is an excellent method for determining pendulum length from the BPM calculated for a movement. This method was explained by Jesse Coleman in *The Best of J.E. Coleman: Clockmaker*, with Mr. Coleman listing his source as Reid's *Treatise on Clock and Watchmaking*. The concept is to start with the known "seconds" pendulum which beats once per second (60 BPM) and is assumed to be 39.2 inches in length (the length varies slightly at different places). This information is compared to the pendulum being studied, which we'll call the student's pendulum. The equation which results is: $(60 \text{ BPM})2 \times 39.2" = (\text{student BPM})^2 \times \text{student length}$. Or: $3600 \times 39.2" = (\text{student BPM})^2 \times \text{student length}$. Since the 3600 x 39.2 is present in every example, the answer of 141,120 is a constant we use every time. Solving for student length is just a matter of dividing the constant 141,120 by the square of the student BPM.

FIG. 87. CALCULATING BEATS PER HOUR AND PENDULUM LENGTH
EXAMPLE 1: ENGLISH MOVEMENT WITH THE CENTER ARBOR IN THE GEAR TRAIN

Beats per Hour and Beats per Minute

$$\frac{60 \times 56 \times 30}{8 \times 7} = \frac{100,800}{56} = 1800 \qquad 1800 \times 2 \text{ pallets} = 3600 \text{ BPH or } 60 \text{ BPM}$$

$$\textbf{Pendulum Length} = \frac{141120}{60^2} = \frac{141120}{3600} = 39.2 \text{ inches, a seconds pendulum.}$$

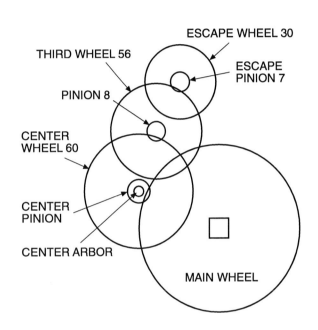

Example 1: Center arbor "in the train". Two examples will show how to count the train and apply the method for calculating pendulum length. Figure 87 illustrates the first example, an English bell strike movement. For purposes of counting the gear train, this movement is similar to most movements in which the center arbor is "in the train". A center arbor that is in the train could not be removed without interrupting the continuous series of gears leading from the main wheel up to the escape wheel.

Only certain gears are involved in the calculation. In this example the center pinion does not figure in the calculations, since it is assumed to turn once per hour. The main wheel (and an intermediate wheel and pinion, if the movement has one) leading into the center pinion are also left out of the calculation. They are used for another purpose— figuring the daily or weekly distance the weight falls or the number of turns made by the spring barrel.

The gear diagram in Figure 87 shows that the drivers in this movement are the center, third, and escape wheels; the driven gears are the pinions on the third arbor and the escape arbor. The example yields the beat of 3600 per hour (BPH), or 60 BPM. Applying the formula for pendulum length produces the result of 39.2 inches, a pendulum which swings once per second. The student should try the calculations with other BPM values and check the results with the table, Figure 89.

Example 2: Auxiliary driven center arbor. Old American movements are the most common examples of the auxiliary driven center arbor. In this design the center arbor is not in the train. In other words, if the center arbor were to be removed from the movement there would still be a continuous path of gears from the main wheel through the escape wheel. Figure 88 on the next page shows the layout of this type of movement.

Calculating the beat of auxiliary drive movements confuses many repairers. They ask why the second wheel is *not* included in the calculation, despite the fact that this wheel is in the gear train and located above the center arbor. The answer is that the sec-

FIG. 88. CALCULATING BEATS PER HOUR AND PENDULUM LENGTH
EXAMPLE 2: AMERICAN CLOCK MOVEMENT WITH AUXILIARY DRIVEN CENTER ARBOR

Beats per hour and Beats per Minute

$$\frac{26 \times 40 \times 40 \times 34}{8 \times 8 \times 8} = \frac{1,414,400}{512} = 2762.5 \qquad 2762.5 \times 2 \text{ pallets } = 5525 \text{ BPH or } 92.083 \text{ BPM}$$

$$\textbf{Pendulum Length} = \frac{141,120}{92.083^2} = \frac{141,120}{8479.28} = 16.64 \text{ inches}$$

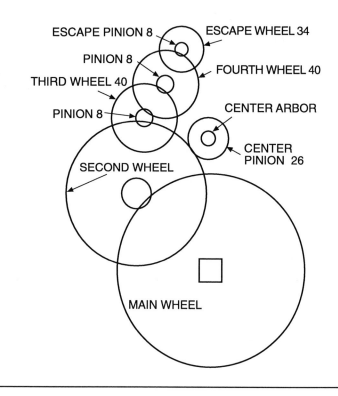

ESCAPE PINION 8 — ESCAPE WHEEL 34
PINION 8
THIRD WHEEL 40 — FOURTH WHEEL 40
PINION 8 — CENTER ARBOR
SECOND WHEEL — CENTER PINION 26
MAIN WHEEL

ond wheel meshes with two gears, the center pinion and the pinion on the third arbor, and it just transfers motion between them. When the second wheel moves a tooth on the third pinion, it also moves a tooth on the center pinion. The two pinions function as though geared directly together.

The center pinion, the brass gear on the center arbor, has a relatively small number of teeth, with 26 being the most common in American clocks. This gear is treated as a wheel in the calculation of beats per hour, so it is placed in the numerator of the fraction with the other wheels.

Figure 89 is a useful table of the pendulum lengths corresponding to beats per minute (BPM) rates ranging from 170 to 60. That covers the range of a shelf clock with a pendulum under 5 inches in length to a grandfather clock with a seconds beat pendulum over 39 inches in length. The figures in

the table were generated from the formula on page 48. Remember that these lengths are "effective pendulum lengths" from the bending point of the suspension spring to the center of mass of the pendulum, not the total length of the pendulum assembly. Total length is often longer by several inches.

Electronic Clock Timers
No discussion of timekeeping is complete without some information about electronic clock timers. Available for some years now, timers have been changing and improving along with the electronics industry.

There is a seemingly infinite number of gear trains in clocks, compared to a relatively few standard beats in mechanical watches. That means the clock repairer has to begin by determining the clock's beat in beats per hour (BPH) as explained in

BPH	BPM	LENGTH (IN.)	BPH	BPM	LENGTH (IN.)
10200	170	4.9	6840	114	10.9
10080	168	5	6720	112	11.3
9960	166	5.1	6600	110	11.7
9840	164	5.2	6480	108	12.1
9720	162	5.4	6360	106	12.6
9600	160	5.5	6240	104	13.1
9480	158	5.7	6120	102	13.6
9360	156	5.8	6000	100	14.1
9240	154	6	5880	98	14.7
9120	152	6.1	5760	96	15.3
9000	150	6.3	5640	94	16
8880	148	6.4	5520	92	16.7
8760	146	6.6	5400	90	17.4
8640	144	6.8	5280	88	18.2
8520	142	7	5160	86	19.1
8400	140	7.2	5040	84	20
8280	138	7.4	4920	82	21
8160	136	7.6	4800	80	22.1
8040	134	7.9	4680	78	23.2
7920	132	8.1	4560	76	24.4
7800	130	8.4	4440	74	25.8
7680	128	8.6	4320	72	27.2
7560	126	8.9	4200	70	28.8
7440	124	9.2	4080	68	30.5
7320	122	9.5	3960	66	32.4
7200	120	9.8	3840	64	34.5
7080	118	10.1	3720	62	36.7
6960	116	10.5	3600	60	39.2

FIG. 89. TABLE OF BEATS PER HOUR, BEATS PER MINUTE, AND PENDULUM LENGTHS.

this chapter. This value is then compared with the readings of BPH produced by the timer attached to the movement. The pendulum or balance is adjusted until the timer's reading agrees as closely as possible with the calculated rate.

Timers operate by picking up the ticking of the clock and converting the sound to pulses. The problem to be overcome by the timer is that many escapements produce various other scraping and squeaking sounds in addition to the noise made by an escape tooth hitting a pallet. The extra sounds are sometimes included in the beat count, producing a false reading. One way to minimize this effect is to grease the crutch of the escapement assembly. Another is to move the sound pickup clamp further away from the escapement, perhaps hooking it onto a winding arbor. Fortunately, timers continue to improve, and the more recent models give very few problems with false readings.

The timer can help the repairer to bring a clock very close to the correct rate—perhaps to within a few minutes of deviation per week—very quickly. This makes it a time saver for repairs and for those occasions when a new pendulum is being fitted to a clock.

Further Reading

Two repair texts which are especially helpful in the area of timekeeping are *The Best of J.E. Coleman: Clockmaker* edited by Orville R. Hagans and *Practical Clock Repairing* by Donald de Carle.

For a complete service procedure on the floating balance escapement described on page 47, see the editor's *Book 3 Escapements* from the *Clockmakers Newsletter Workshop Series*, pages 84—97.

7

STRIKE & CHIME

Strike and chime clocks cause a great deal of apprehension among beginners who are afraid they will not be able to reassemble and adjust them. The endless variety of devices is surprising; one can work on clocks for years and still keep coming across new inventions and variations. Nonetheless, there are several main types of strike and chime mechanisms to learn. Once this is done, most of the different movements crossing the repair bench begin to fall into categories that are understood.

The best approach is to start with striking movements, then progress to chime movements with their added gear train for quarter hour melodies.

Striking Clocks

Striking clocks mark the hour and often the half hour by lifting a hammer to strike a gong, bell, or chime rod. The most common setup is for the movement to strike one blow for one o'clock, two for two o'clock, and so on. The half hour is marked by one strike.

A variation on this system is called the "bim-bam" strike. One strike is made up of a pair of notes—a note of higher pitch followed by another of lower pitch. Twelve o'clock is marked by twelve pairs of notes. Each half hour is marked by a single tone, usually the lower-pitched note.

Another common system is the ship's bell strike. Under this setup, the clock strikes once at 12:30, twice at 1:00, and so on until the count of eight is struck at 4:00. The pattern then starts over, with the count increasing by one each half hour until eight is struck again at 8:00. The last segment of counting ends with eight struck at 12:00. The ship's bell strike simulates the observance of four-hour "watches" on ships. The most interesting aspect of ship's bell clocks, which are a study unto themselves, is the method the movement uses to count the odd numbers: 1, 3, 5, and 7 bells.

Other than these kinds of variations in the striking scheme, the most important difference among striking movements is the method used for counting the strokes of the hammer. The two main counting devices are the count wheel and the rack & snail.

Count wheel strike. The count wheel is a very old device for counting the strike. It is fairly simple in its concept but has the disadvantage of not being able to correct itself. This means that if the strike weight or mainspring runs down or the hands are turned rapidly around, the strike count will no longer match the time indicated by the hour hand. The count wheel strike is only capable of striking a certain count and then locking itself. The next time it is unlocked to strike, it counts the appropriate number of strokes for the next hour or half hour, no matter what has happened to the hands in the meantime.

Figure 90 shows a Gilbert striking movement made in Connecticut in 1926. Its count wheel strike mechanism is a typical example of those found in

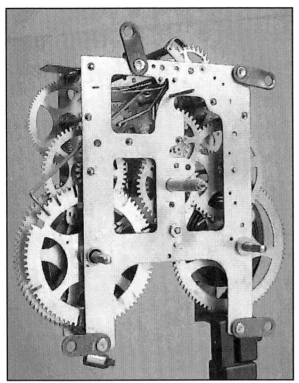

Fig, 90. A Gilbert count wheel strike movement. The strike train is made up of the gears and levers on the left side of the movement. The time train is on the right.

American clocks manufactured during the age of mass-production. This period extended through the second half of the 19th century and continued until its decline in the early 20th century.

The heart of this mechanism is the *count wheel*, a large diameter wheel with deep slots spaced at intervals around the rim. Each deep slot represents the end of an hour count. In Figure 91, the parts

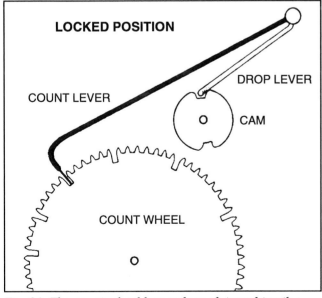

Fig. 91. The count wheel has a deep slot marking the end of each hour strike sequence. Note the progressively longer intervals between the deep slots on the wheel.

which operate with the count wheel are also shown. The *count lever* settles into a slot, ending the strike sequence. The *drop lever* and *cam* are synchronized with the count wheel and permit the count lever to lower itself after each hammer blow. As the clock strikes (Figure 92) the cam keeps the count lever riding above the rim of the count wheel. Each time

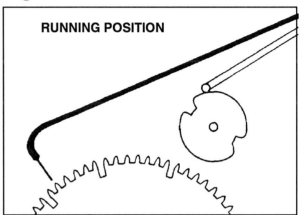

Fig. 92. The cam raises the levers as the clock strikes.

the count lever lines up with the shallow space between two of the teeth, the drop lever allows the count lever to dip into it. This action allows you to watch the mechanism count the hammer strokes.

In some movements, the count wheel is smooth except for the deep slots; the shallow teeth, which are used to drive the count wheel in other movements, are not present. Instead, the smooth count wheel is fastened directly to the main wheel. A few of these wheels by Gilbert count 24 hours in one revolution, although most wheels count only 12 hours.

A count wheel with twelve deep slots counts hours only. If it is the toothed variety, the count wheel will have a total of 78 spaces between the teeth, including the deep slots and shallow tooth spaces. This number is the total of $1 + 2 + 3$ and so on, up through twelve. Some of these movements are still able to strike the half hours with what is called a *passing strike*, an arm on the center arbor which simply lifts and drops the hammer once each half hour. Sometimes the passing strike hits a bell and the hours are struck on a gong.

Many of the American count wheel clocks strike the half hour by counting a note from the count wheel rather than sounding it from a passing strike. This requires the addition of 12 half hour slots, each placed at the end of a strike sequence, increasing the total to 90 teeth for a toothed count wheel. The smooth variety of count can be identified as a half hour striker if the deep slots are double width.

Figure 93 shows the parts involved in transferring the unlocking action from the center arbor to the strike mechanism to start up the strike. The

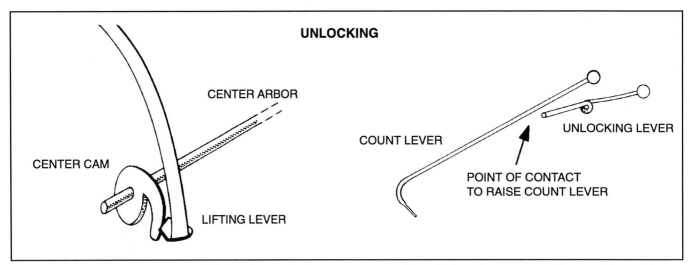

Fig. 93. The center cam raises the lifting lever, which in turn causes the unlocking lever to raise the count lever. This brings the movement to the warning position to await the hour or half hour.

shape of the parts varies in different movements, but the functions are the same.

The count wheel movement must have a way to prepare itself to strike. This action occurs at about seven minutes before the hour or hour and half hour and is called the *warning position* . This leaves the strike gears poised to start without delay at the correct moment. After starting and then running for the correct number of strokes, the strike mechanism must lock itself again. Figure 94 shows the sequence of events as the locking and warning levers perform their functions.

Adjustments are made to the count wheel strike mechanism by bending the levers which are usually made of soft steel wire. A pair of bending tools such as the one shown in Chapter 1 is very useful for this work. Each strike lever can be bent, so it is important to consider the effect of each adjustment before it is made. It can take a skilled repairer hours

to correct a strike movement after someone else has severely bent the levers in an attempt to adjust them.

Several strike adjustments should be considered. Check that the count lever points straight toward the center of the count wheel, bringing the tip of the lever straight into the slots. Bend the lever carefully if necessary. Next, bend the drop lever down if it is necessary to increase the amount of lift it gives to the count lever. This adjustment may be necessary to keep the count lever clear of the count wheel during striking. With the mechanism in the locked position, check that the lock pin is stopped by the locking lever; bend the lever if needed. The warning action is adjusted in a similar way by bending the warning lever so that it catches the lock pin at the moment the clock moves to the warning position. Another adjustment changes the lead time, averaging seven minutes, that the warning occurs before the hour or hour and half hour. By bending the un-

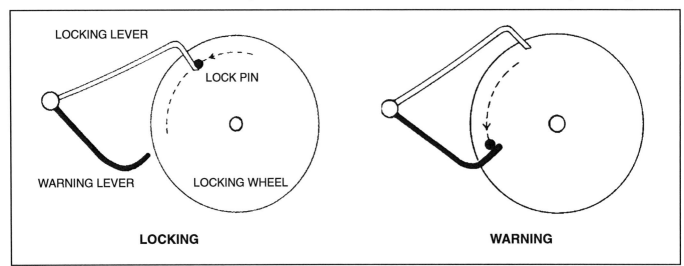

Fig. 94. The locking and warning in a count wheel movement. In the running position, not shown, the levers pivot clockwise; the lock pin and the locking wheel are free to turn without hitting either lever.

locking lever up, you can make the warning occur a few minutes earlier than the present setting. Finally, the moment the strike begins can be changed by bending the end of the lifting lever.

The count wheel strike adjustment procedures described here will give the beginner an idea of the skills that must be learned through practice. Some of the common count wheel arrangements have been described, but there are several variations. An interesting one is the New Haven movement which locks on the cam instead of on the lock pin. The movement uses the pin only as a warning pin. There are many other small differences in design to keep the work interesting.

Rack & snail strike. This type of strike mechanism has an advantage over the count wheel strike. The hour hand stays synchronized with the hour count. The hands can be turned rapidly, without waiting for the strike, yet the count will remain correct; the strike can be allowed to run down, but it will strike correctly when it is wound and restarted. To install the hour hand correctly, the repairer needs to listen for the number of strokes made on the hour and then move the hour hand to point to that hour. Then the actual time can be correctly set using the minute hand. This concept is very difficult to explain over the phone to a customer who has accidentally moved the hour hand out of place!

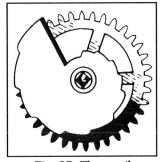

Fig. 95. The snail.

The key to the mechanism is a special cam called the *snail* (Figure 95). Each step on the snail represents a particular hour. A few snails on French clocks are shaped in a continuous curve instead of a series of steps, but they work in the same way. The snail is attached to the hour wheel and geared in with the motion work which drives the hands, so the snail is always ready to control the number of hammer strokes. Owners have to be told that moving the hour hand by itself will not change the time— it just creates an incorrect strike count. It's true that in a few rack and snail striking clocks the hour hand is indexed to the snail and can be turned independently to the hour desired.

Figure 96 shows the Seth Thomas No. 125 movement with rack and snail strike. A similar strike mechanism is found on several Seth Thomas movements fitted in a variety of cases. Despite differences in the shape of the individual parts, rack and snail movements from many styles of clocks, produced in several different countries, all work in basically the same way.

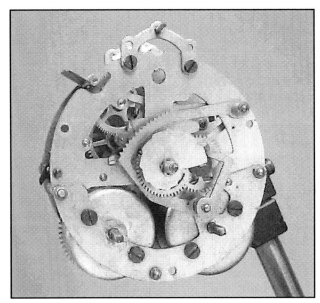

Fig. 96. The Seth Thomas No. 125 balance movement with rack and snail strike from a banjo clock.

Figure 97 is a drawing of some of the main strike parts on the front of a rack and snail movement. The snail from Figure 95 is now matched to a *rack*. Before each hour the tail of the rack drops down to contact the snail; the longer the drop, the more strokes are counted out. The actual counting occurs as the rotating *gathering pallet* (see inset below) engages and gathers up rack teeth one at a time.

A lever called the *rack hook* rests between two rack teeth each time a tooth is moved, holding the

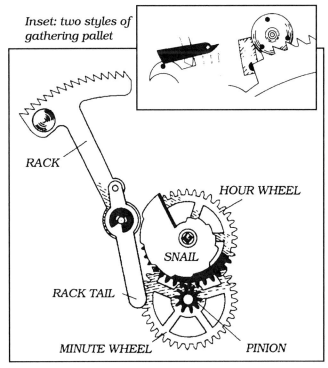

Fig. 97. Parts of the rack and snail mechanism.

rack in place until the next tooth is gathered. Figure 98 shows the rack hook in an English Bell strike movement. The gathering pallet in the drawing is about to pick up another tooth on the rack, with the rack hook holding the rack in place. In this movement, the strike ends when the gathering pallet locks on the *rack pin*, shown as a black dot on the left end of the rack.

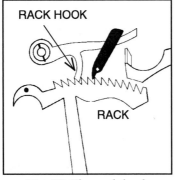

Fig. 98. The rack hook.

The rack and snail mechanism will have a pin wheel of some kind in the movement. It can be a stamped-out "star" which lifts the hammer tail with each of its points, or it can be a set of pins driven into a wheel as shown in Figure 99. The number of points or pins varies from two to 10 or more. It's a rule (almost always true) that the hammer tail should be at rest and not left partly raised when the clock is not striking. The reason: a strike train that starts up with the hammer under load may stall.

Figure 99 also shows the warning wheel and pin. Assemble the gears so the wheel must travel about a half revolution before the pin contacts the warning lever. On some rack and snail mechanisms, however, one pin performs the locking and warning functions. This establishes the warning run as the distance between the locking and warning levers, and no adjustment is needed.

Another important adjustment should be checked in relation to the snail. When the minute hand is turned to the hour, the rack is released so the rack tail falls upon the snail. Always check that the rack tail falls upon the lowest portion of the snail which is for 12 o'clock. Follow through to make sure it also falls cleanly upon the highest portion, for 1 o'clock. If the snail is out of its proper position, the rack tail will jam somewhere along the steep angle between the 12 and 1 o'clock positions. To adjust the snail, remove the washer over the minute wheel pinion. The washer may be held on with a taper pin, a steel snap-on washer, or some other fastener. Pull the hour wheel and snail until the

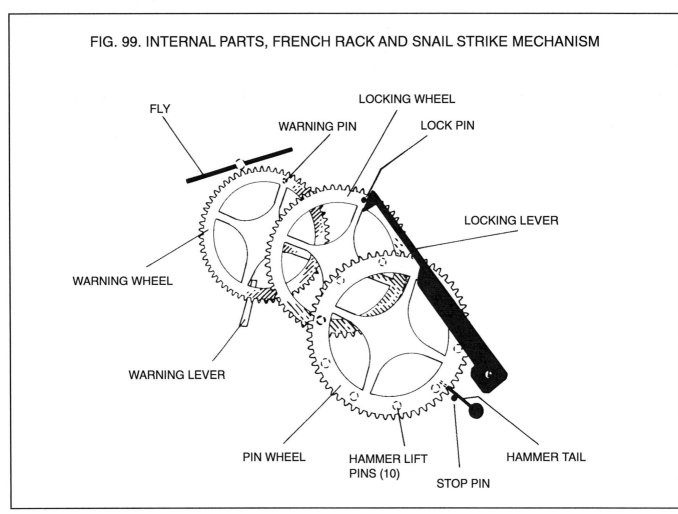

FIG. 99. INTERNAL PARTS, FRENCH RACK AND SNAIL STRIKE MECHANISM

hour wheel teeth come away from the pinion. Change the mesh of the wheel and pinion by one tooth either way and recheck the operation of the snail. This adjustment is essential, since a rack tail that jams on the snail will usually cause the clock to stop between 12 and 1 o'clock.

Chiming Clocks

While striking clocks announce the hour and half hour, chiming clocks add another function: they play a melody, usually based on an English or French cathedral chime, at each 15 minute mark. There are a number of two-train chime movements which have a time train and a dual-purpose chime-strike train. Most movements, however, start with the time train and add separate trains for the strike and

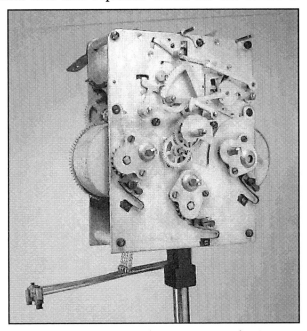

Fig. 100. A Westminster chime movement by Ansonia.

chime functions, making three in all. The usual layout is strike on the left side, time in the center, and chime on the right.

The time, chime, and strike mechanisms are separate but linked. At each of the 15-minute marks, the time train starts up the chime train to play the musical notes for that quarter hour. On the hour only, the chime train starts up the strike train, which proceeds to count out the number of strokes to announce the hour.

Spring, weight, & electric drives. Figure 100 is an American chime movement powered by three barreled mainsprings—one each for chime, strike, and time. Each spring is sized for the work its gear train must do over the period of eight days. This usually results in a very powerful chime mainspring that must be handled with special care. It is common for spring driven chime clocks to give trouble

because the mainsprings have been shortened or allowed to remain dirty. Sometimes incorrect size replacement springs are used by repairers. A spring driven chime clock which stops working correctly after five or six days probably has a mainspring problem that must be corrected.

Weight power is the common power used in chiming grandfather clocks. As a general rule, the heaviest of the three weights is placed on the right side for the chime. The time, in the center location, may be the same weight as the strike on the left. However, in modern grandfather clocks with lyre style pendulums the time weight may be slightly heavier than the strike. Always check the weights, since they may be labeled on the bottom with their locations. If the marks are hand drawn, however, consider that the weights may be mislabeled.

Electric chime clocks, including grandfather clocks, were especially popular early in the 20th century, when it was thought that electricity would completely replace the weight and the mainspring. The new repairer should approach electric clocks with caution, since the wiring is unsafe on many of these clocks. All questionable parts should be replaced or rewired by an expert. There are two general categories of electric chime clocks. In the first type, the electric clock motor runs the time train and constantly winds small mainspring barrels which in turn power the strike and chime gear trains. The other type of electric chime movement also employs a motor drive for the time, but the chime and strike mechanisms are also directly driven by the motor and do not resemble traditional chime and strike mechanisms.

Chime rods & tubular bells. Chime rods struck by the clock's hammers are the common means of producing the tone in a chime clock. Rods can be mounted horizontally, as shown in Figure 101. Rods can also be mounted vertically in a grandfather clock

Fig. 101. Chime rods and hammers in the Ansonia.

case, or even diagonally in certain mantel and wall clock cases.

Made of copper or steel alloys, the rods are pressed into brass fittings. These fittings are normally threaded into a cast iron gong base, although some of the older clocks have rods pressed directly into the base. The base is screwed to the clock case, which acts as a sounding board.

Figure 102 is a cutaway drawing of a chime rod showing the narrow neck at the point the rod emerges from the fitting. This spot could also have been labeled "rod breaks here" because unsupported rods will vibrate and whip around inside the case, and may break off. To prevent damage, rods should always be shimmed with paper or cardboard pieces before the clock is shipped or moved anywhere outside the house it is normally kept.

If a rod has broken off, it is often possible to unscrew the fitting and remove the broken rod, then replace it. Older chime clocks are more difficult to repair. The fittings may have been pressed instead of threaded into the cast iron gong base, making it necessary to consider other repair options. It may be easier to replace the entire gong base and tuned rod set as a unit. Sometimes, however, the resulting tone is a disappointment or the repairer wants to keep the clock original. In such a case, think about rethreading the gong base to receive one or

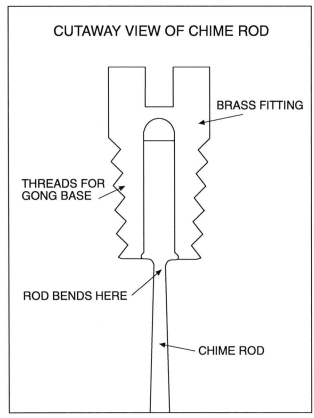

CUTAWAY VIEW OF CHIME ROD

BRASS FITTING

THREADS FOR GONG BASE

ROD BENDS HERE

CHIME ROD

Fig. 102. The chime rod sounds a pleasing tone because of the neck at the point labeled "rod bends here".

more replacement chime rods. The tap required for rethreading is a non-standard 6.4 mm x 1 mm size. Some clock supply sources carry this tap.

A replacement chime rod can be shortened to tune it to the proper pitch. Each time some metal is filed away, the pitch is raised, producing a slightly higher note. It takes practice to be able to tune chime rods. Tuning is often required when a replacement rod is being installed. It is rarely required on an existing rod unless it was tuned incorrectly by someone else.

Some of the largest grandfather clocks chime on tubular bells. These chime clocks were very popular during the period of 1890-1920 and are still produced today in limited numbers. Nine tubular bells are generally for triple chime clocks, those offering a selection of three different chime melodies. Five tubular bells are usually for clocks with Westminster chime only. There are a few clocks with four, six, or other numbers of tubes. Always note the order of the tubular bells before removing them, since different length tubes produce the different pitches required for the melodies.

Chime hammer assemblies. A part called the *pin barrel*, shown in Figure 103, lifts the hammers to play the chime melody. This example from the Ansonia movement is a common type made up of brass disks with hammer-lifting tabs arranged on a shaft. Pin barrels in other movements consist of a brass tube with individual brass pins inserted at the right locations to lift the hammers.

Fig. 103. An Ansonia pin barrel.

The pin barrel is driven by gearing from the chime train. Figure 104 shows the setup on the back of the Ansonia chime movement. In this particular movement, the pin barrel does not lift the hammers directly. Instead, it lifts a set of levers which in turn lift the hammers by tugging on fine brass chains.

It is always necessary to check that a chime clock plays the correct notes. If the sequence turns out to be incorrect because of an assembly error, adjustment is usually accomplished by loosening a set screw in the gearing that drives the pin barrel. The clock is made to chime to a known point, then the gearing is rotated independently to this point and the screw is retightened. From this point on the chimes are correct or at least correctable with the mechanism for self-correction. (See page 60.)

Chime melodies. The simplest approach for the new repairer is to recognize the overall patterns of chime melodies rather than the details of individual

Fig. 104. Part of the Ansonia chime hammer assembly.

chimes. Westminster, the most common chime, is made up of five different combinations (sequences) of the four available notes. The sequences are arranged in this way:

Quarter	Chime Sequence
I	5
II	1, 2
III	3, 4, 5
IV (hour)	1, 2, 3, 4

The first quarter is the 15-minute mark on the dial. It is easy to begin with this quarter because it is represented by one sequence, #5. In addition, this sequence consists of four notes proceeding down the scale. This characteristic makes it possible to set up the chimes without having to read and interpret a written musical score of the melody. Turn the clock hands, pausing to let the clock chime at each quarter. After going through the hour, allowing the clock to self-correct if necessary, turn the minute hand to 15 minutes past the hour. You should hear four descending notes, the pattern of sequence #5. If you do not hear that sequence, it may be necessary to adjust the pin barrel as described earlier.

The other Westminster chime sequences, #1 through #4, are different patterns of the same four notes. It is usually not necessary to know the music behind these other chime sequences in order to set up the clock to chime properly.

Other chimes can be approached in much the same way. Whittington, for example, has twice as many notes, eight per sequence, but its sequence #5 is still made up of descending notes. Dual or triple chime clocks with less-familiar chimes usu-

ally have Westminster or Whittington as one of the selections.

Chime locking plate. Most chime movements have rack and snail striking on the hour. In comparison, the quarter hour chime mechanism is more often a form of count wheel device designed to count only the four quarters. This special count wheel is usually called the *locking plate*.

Figure 105 is a drawing of a locking plate from a movement by Urgos, the German manufacturer. The four quarter hours are marked out to show the increasing length of the chime as one sequence is added at each quarter. Quarter I is played at the 15-minute mark on the dial. The chimes progress through quarter IV, the hour chime. In operation, a lever rides along the rim of the locking plate, keeping the chime train running until it drops into the next slot. This action causes a lock pin to catch on a lever to stop the chime train.

The locking plate usually has the added function of lifting and unlocking the hour strike levers during the hour chime. This lifting action is accomplished in some movements by means of a pin attached to the locking plate. In other locking plates, such as the Kieninger example shown in the inset in Figure 105, the outer rim of the locking plate acts as a cam to raise a lever and unlock the strike.

Locking plates vary greatly in appearance. Recognize them by the presence of the four slots at widening intervals around the rim. Most locking plates are placed on the front of the chime movement. A few movements, such as the Ansonia movement featured in this section, have the locking plate mounted on an arbor between the clock plates. It is harder to see and adjust the locking plate in this location.

Fig. 105. Chime locking plates.

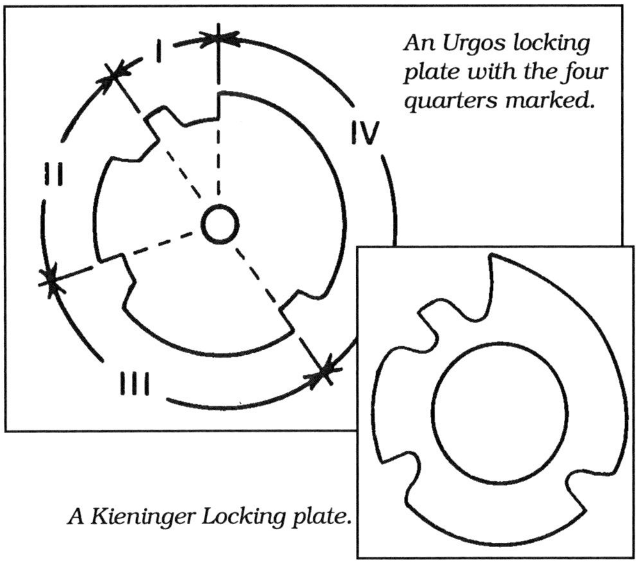

An Urgos locking plate with the four quarters marked.

A Kieninger Locking plate.

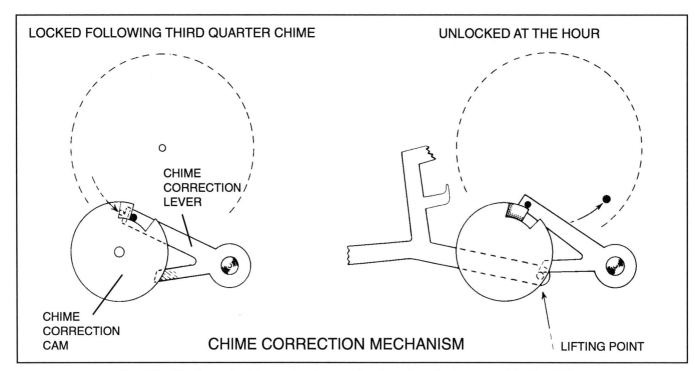

LOCKED FOLLOWING THIRD QUARTER CHIME   UNLOCKED AT THE HOUR

CHIME
CORRECTION
LEVER

CHIME
CORRECTION
CAM   CHIME CORRECTION MECHANISM   LIFTING POINT

*Fig. 106. The Ansonia chime correction mechanism from the movement in Fig. 100.
Adapted from* Chime Clock Repair *by Steven G. Conover, Chapter 9.*

Chime correction. Most locking plate chime mechanisms have a self-correcting device. Although these devices are found in a great many forms, most of them are based on a cam with a single slot. The chime correction cam is mounted behind the locking plate in some movements and on an arbor in other movements.

Most chime correction devices work by allowing the hour chime to operate only on the actual hour, when the minute hand points straight up. As an example, a clock which has had its hands turned rapidly around has just chimed the third quarter melody at 15 minutes past the hour. In the process of self-correction, the movement is silent at the half hour and again at the third quarter. On the hour it resumes correct chiming by playing the hour chime.

A few chime clocks self-correct in a different way. For example, the Herschede tubular bell movement always plays the correct *number* of chime note sequences each quarter hour, but if the hands have been moved rapidly, the clock might play the wrong notes. The clock chimes extra sequences at the hour until a long pin on the pin barrel signals the beginning note of the hour chime. The clock then plays through the correct hour chime melody.

Figure 106 shows the operation of the Ansonia chime correction device following the third quarter chime. In the left-hand drawing, the chime correction lever has dropped into the slot in the chime correction cam. This action places the lever in the path of the chime correction pin and prevents the chimes from working. Only the lifting action at the hour is enough to raise the lever out of the way. In the right-hand drawing this has just occurred, and the hour chime is sounded.

Further Reading

A text on basic clock repair cannot cover all aspects of repairing striking and chiming clocks. The author has written two specialized books to fill this need, *Striking Clock Repair Guide and Chime Clock Repair.*

Those who are interested in chime clock melodies, especially those produced by tubular bell clocks, should obtain a copy of the article "All About Tubular Chime Clocks" by Henry B. Fried in the April 1982 issue, Whole Number 217, of the *Bulletin of the National Association of Watch & Clock Collectors, Inc.*

8

REASSEMBLY, LUBRICATION & TESTING

Being able to reassemble a movement worries many beginners. Experienced repairers are more relaxed about the idea of getting dozens of parts back in the right place, but they worry too, whenever they work on a complicated movement that is new to them.

It's certainly a good idea to take photos or make sketches of your movements before taking them apart. Making some kind of visual record can save a great deal of time and effort later on, during the reassembly phase. It shouldn't be necessary, however, to go to great lengths documenting ordinary movements that are similar to others. After you have done a few American strike movements, for example, you should no longer feel the need to shoot a roll of film over each new one that you repair. Unusual strike and chime movements are a different matter; make a record of at least those aspects of the job that may be forgotten. The locations of certain wheels and levers are examples of hard-to-remember details. The sequence of spacer washers in a chime hammer assembly is another example of the kind of information you'd like to have in front of you when it is time to reassemble a movement.

A Reassembly Procedure

Every movement is different, making it impossible to come up with one procedure that covers all movements. Even movements of a single type can be very different from each other. The sequence in which parts must be installed varies, as does the shape and function of some parts.

Being observant and making helpful notes or sketches is a first step. It is then necessary to decide on a method of reassembly. Look at the movement pillars and the method of mainspring attachment. It is generally easier to assemble the arbors into the movement plate which carries the pillars, rather than the other plate. If the mainsprings are the open type which loop onto the pillars, this is a further reason to place all the parts in the plate with the pillars attached.

There is sometimes a reason to do just the opposite. Figure 107 shows the unassembled Urgos timepiece movement we'll use as an example in this chapter. The pillars are attached to the rear plate, so initially it sounds like a good idea to place all the arbors in that plate. There is a problem with that approach; the center wheel remains attached to the center arbor in the front plate. If all the arbors are placed in the rear plate, it would be quite a trick to fit the center wheel *behind* the second wheel where it belongs. Therefore it is better to assemble this particular movement by placing the arbors in the front plate. It isn't difficult in this case to ease the pillars past the gears when installing the rear plate.

Before installing the second plate, double check that no parts have been left out. If you do accidentally leave out an arbor, especially one with an extra-long pivot on one end, you will have to com-

Fig. 107. The center wheel stays with the front plate of this Urgos movement. For this reason it is better to place the arbors in the front plate, then add the rear plate which supports the movement pillars.

pletely disassemble the movement to correct the error. That isn't much work in a timepiece movement like our example, but it can be a chore in a strike or chime movement.

This brings up the point that reassembly is a patient kind of work that cannot be hurried. Be prepared to take an assembled movement apart again to install a part correctly. It's not unusual to do an assembly task several times before it is correct. It also sometimes happens that a movement goes together easily the first time. The ease of assembly is affected by the design and complexity of the movement and the skill you bring to it.

Now it's time to start the reassembly. Place all the pivots in either the front or rear movement plate—whichever one you have decided is easier. If the movement is powered by mainspring barrels that can be detached from the assembled movement,

then leave them aside until later; they will just get in the way now. If the pallet unit can be left out, that's probably a good idea, too; it will also be in the way. Some movements have a removable pallet bridge that makes it easy to install the pallets at the end of the job.

Consider another special case: the escape wheel. Most clocks require that the escape wheel be installed in the beginning with all the other parts. However, some movements with a visible Brocot escapement should be fully assembled before the center portion of the dial is added, followed by the escape wheel, the escape bridge, and the pallets. In American movements with a front-mounted strip pallet escapement, the escape wheel and arbor must be pre-loaded into the front plate, even if the rest of the arbors are placed in the rear plate.

The parts can generally be assembled in any order that is convenient. It is sometimes necessary to observe a certain order with some parts. For example, some German spring driven movements with non-detachable mainspring barrels must be added before the center arbor is installed. In some movements one gear must be added before others that overlap it.

Once the arbors are loaded into one plate, begin to fit the other plate on top. The task is to carefully fit the pivots into the holes in the second plate. Figure 108 shows that pivots are exposed to possible bending, so care must be taken. Naturally, thinner pivots are more likely to bend than thicker ones. Fit the largest pivots into their holes first; these are usually near the lower end of the plates. When several pivots are in place, see if it is possible to loosely install the nuts or pins on the lower pillars to retain the work that has been done so far.

With fingers or tweezers, reach in to check which unseated pivots are under slight tension between

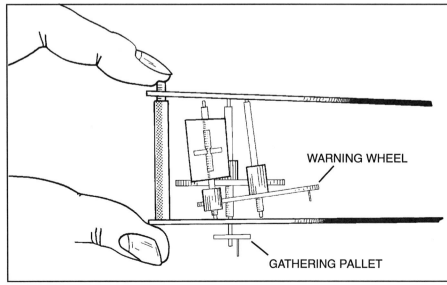

WARNING WHEEL

GATHERING PALLET

Fig. 108. During the assembly process, individual arbors are cocked at an angle until the pivots are fitted into the holes in both plates. There is some danger of bending pivots, so avoid forcing them. It may be necessary to separate the plates again slightly to correct the mesh of certain strike or chime wheels and pinions. This drawing, adapted from Chime Clock Repair, was made to show how a strike warning wheel is eased out of place to allow its pinion to be meshed correctly with the wheel on the gathering pallet arbor.

Fig. 109. Use fingers or tweezers to ease the pivots into the holes. Tighten the pillar nuts gradually as you proceed to assemble the movement.

the plates. You may feel that one pivot, more than any others, is keeping the plates apart; fit this one next. As the plates come together (Fig. 109) gradually add the upper nuts and tighten them just finger tight. If taper pins are used in the pillars, install them as soon as possible with the fingers.

In some cases it is helpful to leave out one or two arbors until the plates are partly assembled. An example is a fly arbor that repeatedly falls out because it is near the top of the movement, where the plates are furthest apart as the work proceeds. Install the arbor when it is still possible to fit it in without placing the pivots under stress.

View the movement from several angles (Fig. 110) and be certain that all the pivots are seated in the holes before tightening the pillar nuts or taper pins. Tightening the plates together with a pivot out of its hole will result in a bent or even a broken pivot. It

Fig. 110. Double check that all pivots are in the holes before tightening the pillar nuts or (in other movements) pressing in the taper pins.

takes only a moment to check each arbor for endshake, the back-and-forth play that confirms the pivots are seated in the holes.

In strike and chime movements, some or all of the levers may be added to the movement so the mechanism can be checked for correct assembly. Now is the time to partially separate the plates again, if necessary, to correct the way a pinion and its neighboring wheel mesh together.

Detachable mainspring barrels can be added next, but make sure the pillar nuts or taper pins are tight before winding the mainsprings even part of the way. Figure 111 shows a typical setup for a detachable mainspring barrel in a modern movement. The barrel and winding arbor are installed using the slot in the front plate. The click wheel is pushed onto the winding arbor, then the ratchet cover is positioned and held with a set screw. Other

Fig. 111. A detachable mainspring barrel can be added after the movement plates are completely assembled. Note the slot which permits removal and installation.

movements use a similar setup in which the winding arbor is keyed to slide into the barrel arbor; there is no slot in the front plate. The ratchet cover is still used to hold the assembly together.

Movements with open, loop-end style mainsprings have some kind of wire retainer to contain them during handling and assembly. When the movement is fully assembled and the pillar nuts or taper pins are tight, wind the springs partially to loosen the retainers. Then angle them out of the movement; they have served their purpose.

All the remaining movement parts should now be added. Typically, the pallets, motion work gears, suspension spring, and pendulum hanger are needed. Figure 112 shows front and rear views of the completed Urgos movement. This happens to

 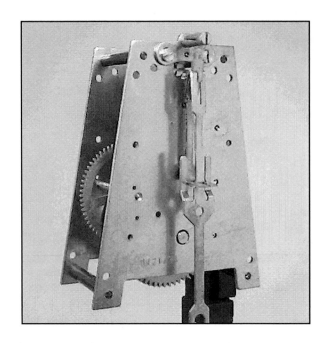

Fig. 112. Two views of the assembled Urgos movement. The front view (left) shows the motion work gears and the ratchet wheel and cover. The rear of the movement (right) supports the pendulum suspension unit.

be a simple timepiece movement, but it does demonstrate that certain parts are added after the plates are fully assembled, and all the pivots are seated in the holes.

Lubrication

Today's clock oils and greases, especially the synthetic lubricants, are better than those of the past. Old-time lubricants lasted only a year or two before turning waxy and drying out; the clock stopped and had to be cleaned and oiled again. Modern lubricants are capable of lasting for years without drying up.

Experience shows that the best treatment a clock can receive is periodic cleaning and oiling. The next best procedure is to make sure a clock is oiled every few years, even if it is not cleaned until it is quite dirty. The worst plan is to run a clock until it stops after a number of years. This results in extra wear because dry pivots wear quickly. The most extreme examples of damage resulting from dry pivots are found in electric clocks. The motor is often strong enough to keep turning a dry pivot until it wears through and snaps off! Fortunately, most weight or spring driven clocks will stop before such severe damage occurs. Still, the damage will not occur in the first place if the clock is kept oiled.

Almost any modern clock oil and grease should perform well, but by trying various brands, you will develop preferences. Clock repairers can become almost superstitious in feeling that only one oil will keep their clocks going. Try a few; you might even decide that one type is better for modern clocks and

another suits you better for antiques.

Some repairers go to great lengths to save on the cost of lubricants by using ordinary oils not designed for clocks. This is unwise and it does not save money in the long run if clocks have to be redone as a result of poor performance. Other repairers mix their own concoctions, especially for mainsprings. I don't think it is worth the effort; I have not had clocks returned as a result of using commercial mainspring lubricants. Price may be a factor in deciding which lubricants to use, but it should not be the main factor. After all, the quantity used is small.

The actual technique used for oiling clocks is easy to master. Most clocks have oil sinks, recesses cut into the plate around the pivot hole. Use an oiler, which may be a commercial product or a piece of soft wire hammered flat on one end. Dip it into a clean oil cup filled with oil, not into the bottle. Apply enough oil to partially fill the oil sink, but do not let it flow over the top and run down the plate. Over-oiling is a messy practice that allows most of the oil to be drawn out of the pivot hole and away from the pivot where it is needed. Apply grease sparingly to levers and other surfaces, and avoid smearing it with your fingers.

Mainsprings are oiled using two methods. Some repairers like to apply the mainspring oil (or grease) with a rag and carefully wipe it over all the coils. I prefer to install the spring in the barrel or attach it to the movement pillar first, then apply the oil, making it unnecessary to handle oily springs. Mainspring oil applied across the coils is distributed over the coils as the spring is wound and unwound.

Here is a list of lubrication points for clocks, some of which are illustrated below:

•Oil all pivot holes
•Oil the pallet faces
•Grease or oil the crutch
•Grease or oil a few of the ratchet teeth
•Place a drop of oil at the click rivet or screw
•Oil the barrel bushing holes
•Oil or grease the hand clutch
•Oil the click spring where it contacts the click
•Grease the hammer dampers
•Grease the hammer tails
•Grease the hammer lifting star
•Grease the pins or star cam (or pins).
•Grease the chime or strike levers where they rub or slide on others
•Oil the bearings of a pulley

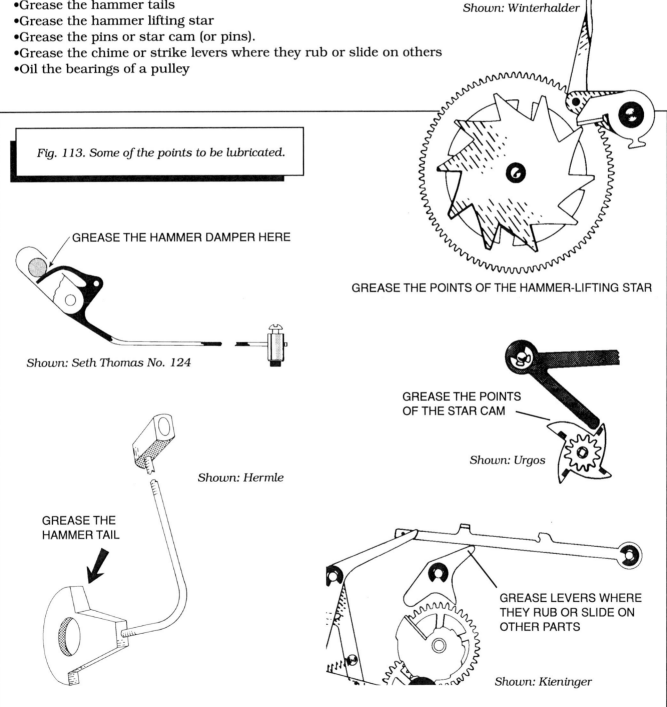

Shown: Winterhalder

Fig. 113. Some of the points to be lubricated.

GREASE THE HAMMER DAMPER HERE

Shown: Seth Thomas No. 124

GREASE THE POINTS OF THE HAMMER-LIFTING STAR

GREASE THE POINTS
OF THE STAR CAM

Shown: Urgos

Shown: Hermle

GREASE THE
HAMMER TAIL

GREASE LEVERS WHERE
THEY RUB OR SLIDE ON
OTHER PARTS

Shown: Kieninger

Do not lubricate:
•Gear teeth
•Pinions of either lantern or leaf type
•Hammer assemblies (see below)
•The hour pipe of an American clock
•Hairsprings

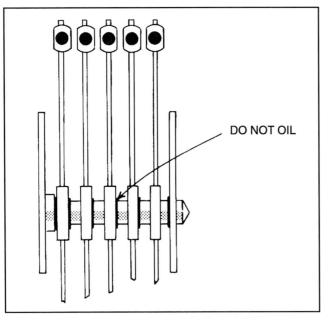

DO NOT OIL

Fig. 114. Hammers pivot on a shaft in the hammer assembly. This assembly should be clean, but if it is oiled it may become sticky after a year or two.

Testing

Individual clock repairers differ greatly in their approach to testing. At one end of the spectrum, some repairers say that no "out of the case" testing should be needed if the work has been done carefully. They case up the movement, add the hands and dial, and adjust the hammers. The test run is only a few days in length.

Those at the other extreme set up the movement on a benchtop or floor test stand and run it for an extended period of weeks. Finally, it is cased and run further before it is delivered to the customer.

The best approach to testing is more flexible. If it takes only a few minutes to install a movement in the case, you might want to skip bench testing and set the clock up right away. Other clocks which need troubleshooting work may need to be seen from all angles on a test stand. For many repairs, a few days on a test stand can be followed by a longer period of running in the case.

In the end, the only true test of a movement is to run it in the case in the same way the customer will run it. Testing in the case certainly makes it easier to detect strike or chime errors because the clock can be heard. It is also easier to regulate a clock when the dial is present. Finally, there might be something about the case that you would want to know right away. Examples are dials that rub on some part of the movement, moon phase mechanisms that bind, narrow case bottoms that are tapped by the swinging pendulum, and rattling gongs or chime rods.

Test stands have been designed in many configurations to suit the tastes of the repairer. Check with your supplier to learn what is available to meet your needs. You might even want to design and make your own test stands instead. The problem with test stands in general is that it is difficult to find or make one that will handle a full range of movements. Several stands could be used for mantel and wall clock movements and another used for floor clock movements. Having three or more test stands could run into too much investment, not to mention the need for floor and bench space to accept them.

When you start a clock on test, wind it fully and note the day and time on a piece of paper to be kept near the clock. Use a timer to regulate the clock quickly, or make successive adjustments to correct the rate. It's important to observe whether the clock strikes or chimes correctly. This may seem easy enough, but it is hard to keep track of a number of clocks all sounding at about the same time. The professional repairer who is testing many clocks of different types must be systematic. If he or she is not organized in a method of testing clocks, the work may end up being returned to the customer with defects. It's far easier to note the problems and correct them the first time.

9

ELECTRIC CLOCKS

With the technical assistance of Tom Wining

Fig. 115. Seth Thomas "Sharon" electric striking clock with disassembled parts displayed in front of the case.

A strong warning is needed for anyone who would like to work on electric clocks:
Be careful—electricity can kill!
Repairers must be responsible for their own safety at all times, and this includes safe behavior around electricity. This chapter provides some basic introductory background on common types of electric movements and motors. Those who intend to learn the repair of electric clocks will have to make a much more in-depth inquiry into the subject than this book can provide.

Here are a few basics of electric clock safety. Do not risk electrocution by plugging in an electric clock motor and holding it in your hand. Do not touch a motor with a screwdriver. Work in a dry area and be sure to cover a concrete floor with a rubber or vinyl mat. Replace any motor which has crumbling, dried-out lead wires. Never use a clock with a bad power cord—many have very old wires with cracked plugs. Note: this list of cautions could not possibly list all the hazards of working with electricity.

Electric clocks have been around since the early years of the 20th century. There was a time, back then, that many in the industry were certain that electric clocks would completely replace weight and spring driven clocks. But after their heyday in the 1920s was over, electric clocks declined rapidly.

Unfortunately, very little technical information has survived on electric clocks, and there are only a few specialists who are experts in this field. There is another factor at work—many of the clocks that still exist contain unsafe motors with frayed cords and bad insulation. The hobbyist who enters this situation needs to move cautiously.

On the plus side, clock suppliers can provide certain parts, and specialists can often help with a reworked or replacement motor to give new life to an old electric clock.

Seth Thomas A300-Powered Clocks

The Model A300 is a common motor found in many Seth Thomas electrics. For example, Figure 115 is a striking model; Figure 116 is a chime movement based on the No. 124 mechanical movement. The motor is powerful enough to keep the gears turning in some of the clocks until a dry pivot rusts through and snaps off. Despite this strength, a dirty motor may not keep accurate time, or it may stop. It is, therefore, recommended that the motor be cleaned and lubricated when the movement is repaired. Tom Wining, the electric clock rotor specialist, recommended the following service procedure first published in *Clockmakers Newsletter*. All repairs are done with the power cord unplugged.

Begin by removing the three mounting screws and taking the motor (Figure 117) from the movement. The rotor and shaft can now be taken out. First take note that there is endshake in the shaft; this "play" will have to be maintained after the motor is disassembled and reassembled.

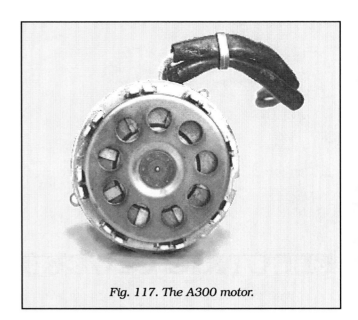

Fig. 117. The A300 motor.

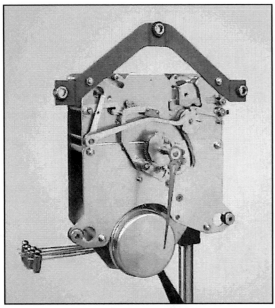

Fig. 116. This Seth Thomas B1703 movement is powered by an A300 motor. Another type of motor, the Sangamo, was also used in this series.

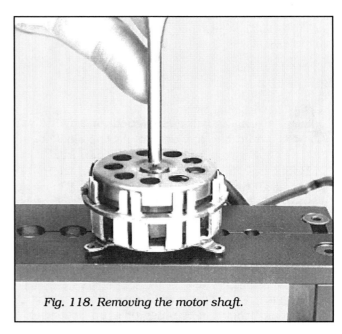

Fig. 118. Removing the motor shaft.

To disassemble the motor, place it on a split stake as shown in Figure 118, with the drive pinion facing down. A few light taps will drive out the shaft, separating it from the rotor. The disassembled motor will now look like Figure 119. Look for the steel washer at the end of the shaft opposite the pinion. The washer's dimensions are: outer diameter .150"; hole .058" diameter; and thickness .006".

A hole with a bearing at each end to support the motor shaft goes all the way through the motor. To clean the motor it is necessary to wipe away the dirt and old lubricant from this area. Apply a small amount of a solvent such as hairspring cleaner. A piece of wire will help to loosen the foreign material.

Lubricate the bearing holes with a clock oil rated to be heat resistant, then reassemble the motor by staking the rotor onto the shaft. Don't forget to in-

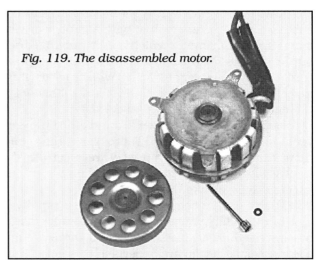

Fig. 119. The disassembled motor.

stall the steel washer, making sure that the original amount of endshake is present in the shaft.

If the Seth Thomas A300 motor does not work properly after this servicing has been completed, it will have to replaced with a refurbished motor.

More About the Seth Thomas Movements

A noteworthy feature of the two Seth Thomas movements discussed so far is that they are basically just familiar types of mechanical movements adapted for electric motor drive. This sets them apart from another type we will look at later in the chapter.

The time train of this style of Seth Thomas movement is driven directly by the motor through a train of gears. The gears are set up so a pinion drives the next wheel. This is the opposite of most horological gearing and is necessary so that the higher speed of the motor can be reduced to turn the hands at the required slower rate.

To drive the strike train and (if so equipped) the chime train, the movements have a small mainspring drive for each added train. Geared into the time train, the small, pocketwatch-size mainspring is contained in a capsule of about 1-1/4" diameter called a spring box (see Figure 120). The outer end of the mainspring is not fastened to the wall of the spring box. Instead, the spring has a thicker piece of steel fastened to it. This thicker part rides against the inside wall of the box, acting as a slip clutch. When the spring has been fully wound by the clock motor, which is normally the case, the entire mainspring rotates very slowly in the spring box. The ability to slip keeps the clock from stalling. The mainspring runs down only if the hands are turned through a number of strike or chime points. The clock will wind the spring up again if left alone to run for a few hours. In the meantime, however, the spring can always be manually wound up by means of a small key included with the clock.

It is important to run the mainsprings completely down before disassembling the movement. The springs are small but can still cause damage if the plates are separated with the springs under power. The best way to run the springs down is to tie up the strike and chime levers and allow the gear trains to run continuously for a few minutes.

Servicing the spring box. The spring box can be opened to allow the spring to be serviced. Servicing should include the addition of fresh graphite, never oil, into the spring box. Graphite of the type used on locks maintains a constant slip factor. Oil is not used because it seems at first to cause the end of the mainspring to slip too much, robbing power. When the oil finally gets gummy it prevents slipping and stops the clock.

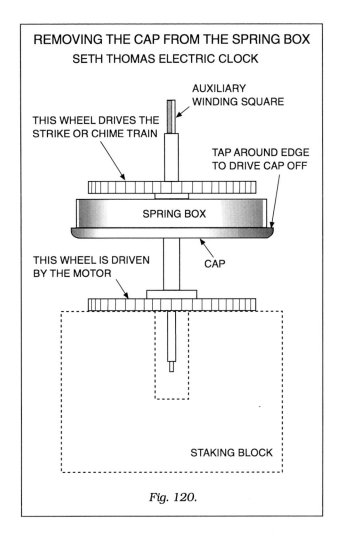

REMOVING THE CAP FROM THE SPRING BOX
SETH THOMAS ELECTRIC CLOCK

AUXILIARY WINDING SQUARE

THIS WHEEL DRIVES THE STRIKE OR CHIME TRAIN

TAP AROUND EDGE TO DRIVE CAP OFF

SPRING BOX

THIS WHEEL IS DRIVEN BY THE MOTOR

CAP

STAKING BLOCK

Fig. 120.

The spring box has a cap which must be removed. The easiest way to remove it is to place the arbor in a hole in the staking block (Figure 120). With a rectangular drift, tap around the edge of the cap until it is free. The cap will drop onto the winding wheel, although it cannot be taken completely off the arbor. Fresh graphite can be added at this point.

If it is necessary to clean the mainspring before lubricating it as described above, the spring box with the mainspring can be turned to release the inner end of the spring from the arbor. Once the eye is free of the hook, remove the spring from the spring box, clean it, and finally replace it in the box before applying the graphite.

Telechron-Powered Clocks

This section covers a different style of movement and motor. Figure 121 shows a General Electric grandfather clock movement, identical to those sold by Herschede. This kind of movement differs from the Seth Thomas style because it does not have the indirect spring drive for the strike and chime trains. The movement utilizes direct motor drive for the strike, chime and time functions. This makes the

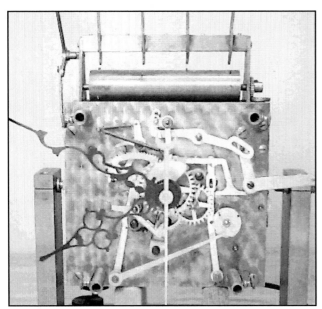

Fig. 121. General Electric tubular chime movement.

repairer's task more difficult; the movement is not a mechanical style modified for electric timekeeping, but a completely special design. The repairer cannot rely very much on previously learned clock repair skills, since this style of electric clock seems to have been designed from scratch. Movements of this type depend upon opposing coil springs and interlocking control levers. Adjustment procedures are very difficult to work out unless the design is completely understood.

Repairers may see the names General Electric, Revere, Telechron, or Herschede on movements of this type. A helpful service guide, *Revere Clocks Service Manual*, has been reprinted and is available from some suppliers. The booklet presents specific adjustment procedures for these mantel and grandfather clock movements. See Chapter 1 for more source information.

The motor is made up of several components, and the Telechron rotor (Figure 122) is perhaps the most misunderstood part. The rotor is made up of a

Fig. 122. The Telechron rotor M3538 from the grandfather clock movement shown in Fig. 121.

lubricated gear train with an output shaft on one end. The internals are enclosed by an aluminum container. The rotor has about a ten-year service life and is not repairable by anyone other than a specialist. Indeed, there is no reason to try a repair if the rotor can simply be replaced with a new one. The repairer's hope is to locate the correct rotor from a supplier's stock. The research being done to reconstruct some of the lost data on electric clocks should make it possible to obtain more parts, thus making it easier to work on these clocks in the future. For now, note the number from the worn rotor and contact a specialist or your clock supplier to determine whether a new rotor is available.

The other parts of the motor are drawn in Figure 123. In addition to the rotor already described, the motor includes an armature made up of a core and a field coil. The field coil generates magnetic fields in the armature. It is necessary to replace the field

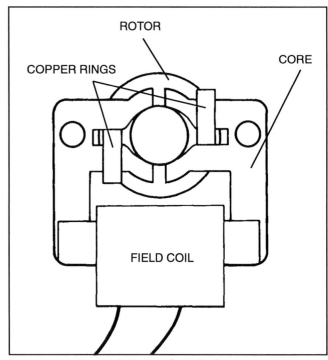

Fig. 123. Parts of a Telechron motor.

coil if the wires are frayed. The copper rings establish the direction of rotation and enable the motor to be self starting.

As with other types of clock motors, do not touch them when they are plugged in. House current is dangerous, especially when a motor of unknown condition is connected to it.

More Electric Clock Repair Hints

It has already been suggested that questionable wiring components should always be replaced in electric clocks. A few other basic repair hints on the next page will help those who would like to work on electric clocks.

There has to be a safe wiring connection made between the lead wires from the field coil and the power supply cord. Several different methods are used to splice the wires together. Wire nuts are often used, but it is essential that they fit—a wire nut that falls off leaves a dangerous bare connection. A better method is to splice the wires together, solder them, then place heat-shrink tubing over the connection. The result is neat and safe. Connections wrapped with electrical tape are not safe and should never be used.

The cord must be anchored in the clock case so that someone cannot tug on the power cord and pull apart the wiring connection or loosen the lead wires in the field coil. Anchoring the cord is a safety requirement that must not be overlooked. In many of the Telechron motors, the power supply cord is knotted around one of the movement pillars to prevent the cord from being pulled through. In other clocks, the power cord is given a loose knot inside the case; it isn't very elegant but it does the job. In Seth Thomas and other mantel clocks with different motors, a screw clamp is used to lock down the cord. This is a positive and safe way of fastening the cord.

Another important point is that electric clocks, like their weight and spring driven relatives, need to be oiled periodically. Running any clock with dry pivots causes extra wear, and eventually the clock will stop. Electric clocks are slightly different in this regard. The motors which power them are sometimes able to keep going for an extended period of time, even after serious damage occurs in a movement that has not been oiled. Figure 124 shows a

Fig. 124. Two wheels from a Seth Thomas electric clock. The wheel on the left has had the teeth ground away because the motor kept going after a pivot sheared off, dropping the wheel out of position. The dark-colored wheel on the right is a fiber wheel which meshes with the brass drive pinion on the motor shaft.

wheel which was damaged when a rusty, dry pivot sheared off, dropping this wheel downward. The motor kept running, unattended, even though the clock no longer kept time. It may have taken weeks to grind the teeth of this wheel almost to a knife-edge. The lesson is simple—electric clocks must be oiled every few years to prevent severe damage from happening.

Electric clock repair and collecting is a fascinating field to enter. There is a great deal of history to learn along with the repair techniques for different types of motors and movements. A surprising variety of electric clocks still survives today, waiting to be rediscovered.

The author sincerely appreciates the help of Tom Wining, whose technical knowledge made this chapter possible.

10

FIVE STARTER CLOCKS

Most repairers start out by working on the clocks that are available to them. This may sound obvious, but it's worth thinking about. A non-working clock belonging to family or friends comes to the attention of the would-be repairer, who proceeds to try to fix whatever is wrong with it. Sometimes it is one of these clocks that actually kindles the person's interest in clock repairing. Others hear of the new repairer's early success and bring other clocks for repair. This is how many hobbyists get started. Unfortunately, it's also a way to get in over your head—a bad place to be if you have no one to bail you out of repair difficulties.

Rather than just take on whatever clock comes into view, the new repairer should think more carefully about what kinds of clocks he or she will repair. Perhaps a list of clocks to avoid should come first. Generally avoid valuable heirloom clocks: it would be unfortunate to seriously damage a clock instead of gaining some skills first and then repairing it safely the next year. Steer clear of any highly valuable piece, no matter who owns it. Avoid most French clocks because of their fine, hardened pivots which may be broken so easily. Balance movements, especially jeweled ones, should also be postponed until some instruction has been taken.

Another suggestion is to avoid repairing for money until you have studied and worked on your own clocks. That doesn't mean you should just go into business and work for free. Learn and practice first! Once the people around you learn of your bud-

ding interest, they may ask you to do repairs for them. Resist the temptation to jump in too quickly and take on too much.

How are you supposed to get started, you ask? Begin by learning some of the basics. Take an evening adult education course, enroll in a correspondence course, or join a collectors' group to locate others who share your interest. Then select a family clock that everyone agrees is not precious. If you begin with a $100 clock that no one thought would ever work again, you are on the right path. An alternative is to start collecting modestly priced clocks by purchasing them in flea markets, antique stores, auctions, or collectors' marts.

The Ansonia clock shown below is an example of a 1920's clock that might easily come into your

Fig. 125. Not a starter clock: Ansonia chime tambour.

hands through one of the two routes just suggested—as a family clock (this one came from my aunt) or a flea market purchase. It is not, however, going to be one of the five starter clocks featured in this chapter. The Ansonia case contains the heavy chime movement pictured in Chapter 7, Figure 100. It is definitely better for the beginner to set it aside if there are other less complicated clocks to choose from. The movement contains three powerful barreled mainsprings and has offset, geared winding mechanisms with many parts. Once a few other chime clocks have been mastered, the Ansonia would be an interesting job for the repairer with one or two years of experience to tackle.

Figure 126 shows an Ingraham black mantel clock that was one of my first flea market purchases. As I recall, it cost about $12.00. This is an excellent starter clock, a type that will be featured in this chapter. The black wood case was in such bad condition that it needed to be refinished. The paper dial and the hands had to be replaced. The movement was the first American time and strike that I disassembled. Unfortunately, I followed some advice in an old repair book. The author had evidently not heard about let-down keys (Chapters 1 and 2) because he suggested raising the click and using the clock's own key to let the mainsprings down a few ratchet teeth at a time. On the third turn, the key slipped from my hand and the mainspring let loose with a bang! Incredibly, neither the movement nor my hand sustained any serious injury. I learned a great deal from that clock. It still runs on the mantel today.

By carefully choosing the clocks you work on, you will be able to learn more easily and avoid discouragement from taking on too much too quickly.

Fig. 126. The author's starter clock: Ingraham "Nemo".

Soon enough you will feel able to take on general repairs for family and friends, if that is your goal. Many people have decided it is better to collect and repair just your own personal clocks. Collectors specialize on a favorite type, such as American clocks, or even a specific brand, such as Seth Thomas. Collecting and repairing certainly complement each other, although some collectors do not repair. Most repairers have at least a small collection of clocks.

The five "starter" clocks described in this chapter are not by any means the only clocks that one should work on first, but they all have certain characteristics that make them good choices. Lower-priced examples of these types should be available in most areas.

The starter clocks are displayed beginning on the next page.

OG CLOCK

The OG is an American shelf clock that gets its name from the s-shaped curved molding on the case. This style was made in large numbers in the 19th and early 20th centuries. The clock shown in Figure 127 is a 26" tall, weight driven, thirty-hour OG,

Fig. 127. Thirty-hour OG striking clock, 26" high.

the most common version. There are some OG's which are larger or smaller, some with eight-day movements, some with alarms, and a few with spring instead of weight drive.

This particular OG is fitted with a painted metal dial (Figure 128). Like most OG dials, this one has a large center hole which gives a view of part of the movement. The clock's label (Figure 129) was preserved under clear plastic by an earlier owner. Labels in old American clocks provide a fascinating insight into the clock industry.

Another interesting feature of OG clocks is the tablet in the lower part of the door. The tablet may be a mirror, a piece of etched glass, or a reverse painting. Tablet pictures exist in a great variety of subjects including portraits, pictures of flowers, and outdoor scenes including famous buildings. Most of the tablets have suffered some damage over the years, and some of them have been replaced with modern reproduction scenes.

Advantages. The typical OG movement offers the beginner an opportunity to work on a count wheel controlled American movement with a recoil strip pallet escapement. Prices of OG clocks have remained relatively low for the most part, making them good investments for new repairers. Parts such as

Fig. 128. Detail of the painted metal dial.

dials, hands, weights, weight cords, pallet units, suspension rods, and replacement glass tablet pictures are available from clock parts suppliers. The weight drive is easier to work with than a powerful mainspring drive, relieving the beginner of having to worry about handling powerful mainsprings.

Disadvantages. On the negative side, many OG clocks have seen hard use over a long period of time and may be badly worn as a result. Years of daily winding has probably taken its toll on the dial, the winding squares, the ratchet assemblies, and even the clock's door. Missing veneer and chipped case corners are found in most OG clocks.

Technical Features. OG clocks have an unusual weight drive which makes maximum use of the height of the case. One end of the weight cord is knotted in the winding drum; from there, the cord leaves the movement diagonally and stretches over a small wooden pulley in the top of the case. The other end of the weight cord hangs down from the pulley, and the weight is attached to a hook. With

Fig. 129. The label identifies George Brown as the maker. Brooks Palmer's book A Treasury of American Clocks *lists Brown as active from 1859-68.*

Fig. 130. The "George Brown" case contains a standard thirty-hour OG striking movement.

Fig. 131. A view of the recoil strip pallet escapement.

this design, the weight can descend from almost the top of the case to the bottom. Incidentally, all the OG pulley does is redirect the cord. It does not act like the pulleys described in Chapter 3, which utilize heavier weights in exchange for reducing the required weight fall.

Figure 130 shows the overall layout of the thirty-hour OG movement. The time train has only the main wheel, second wheel, and escape wheel. An eight-day version can be spotted easily because there will be an additional large wheel before the escape wheel.

Figure 131 shows the strip pallet recoil escapement, a good first challenge for the repairer. The weight provides plenty of power to the escape wheel, keeping the mechanism going even if it is not in the best condition. The pallets are likely to be pitted and should be repaired as described in Chapter 5. The OG clock shown had excessive drop and slightly worn pallets, but it ran despite these problems.

Part of the strike mechanism is shown in Figure 132. There are only two large wheels geared into the train—the main (pin) wheel and the locking wheel. The count wheel is mounted as a loose friction fit behind the main wheel and is advanced by an extra-long pin on the lantern pinion above it. Locking is accomplished by the drop lever hooking in the slot in a cam. The warning lever is a short wire extended out from the fly arbor.

Typical Repairs. There are a number of repairs that are often required in OG clocks. Pivot polishing and bushing work are almost always needed, followed by the escapement repairs just mentioned. Weight cords will have to be replaced in many OG clocks. Check the soft steel strike levers for unusual wear; file and polish as needed to restore smooth

surfaces. Line up the tip of the count lever so that it points straight into the slots in the count wheel. Pay particular attention to the locking action of the drop lever. Adjust the lever so that it locks safely in the cam, yet allows the strike train to run.

There is always the possibility that more difficult repairs will be needed on an OG movement. The example selected for this chapter works well enough, yet I soon noticed that a damaged ratchet tooth had simply been filed off!

Assembling the OG movement is made easier by the fact that the parts are large and relatively few in number. It can still be difficult to get the strike train assembled properly, however. Unlike most American striking clocks, the OG must have the pin wheel meshed just right to assure that the hammer will be at rest when the striking stops.

Fig. 132. Detail view of the strike train.

AMERICAN COUNT WHEEL STRIKING CLOCK

One of the easiest clocks to find is the American spring driven striking clock. Factories such as Seth Thomas, Ansonia, Gilbert, New Haven, and others were especially active from the mid-19th century onward, producing a great variety of styles to attract the buying public. Some of the case styles were revivals of earlier clocks: steeples, banjos, bracket clocks, and others. Other styles, such as the New Haven "black mantel" clock shown in Figure 133, were originated during this clock manufacturing "boom". The Gilbert clock in Figure 133 was made in the 1920's, towards the end of the era. The inevitable "bust" for the American clock industry came during the Great Depression in the 1930's.

For the repairer, the happy result of all this manufacturing is an extensive supply of surviving American striking clocks. The movements were made in different styles, but the common version we are concerned with here is the eight-day, spring driven, count wheel striking movement. Figure 134 shows the movement from the Gilbert clock in Figure 133.

The American striking clock was made with thin wheels and plates, but was powered with strong, eight-foot-long mainsprings that were usually between .016" and .018" thick. The extra power kept most of the movements running for many years with just an occasional oiling. Wear was inevitable, however, and today these clocks are the "bread and butter" of many clock repair shops.

For the collector-repairer, prices of these clocks vary considerably according to the particular style and the condition of the clock. Clocks such as the two pictured in Figure 133 are among the less expensive examples; they were not expensive when they were new!

Advantages. An initial advantage of American eight-day striking clocks has already been mentioned: they are plentiful and sometimes relatively low in price. Repairers will find many new parts available for these movements, with a varying extent of modifications being necessary to fit them. These parts include hands, dials, mainsprings, pallet units, arbors with lantern pinions, escape wheels, and main wheels. More specialized parts, such as strike levers and specialized gears, cannot be purchased new. There are, however, many incomplete or damaged examples of some movements available for parts. A repairer can advertise to purchase movements or parts or attend a sale to locate a dealer who specializes in old movements.

Disadvantages. Many American striking clocks have suffered bad repair work in the past. Profes-

Fig. 133. A Gilbert striking mantel clock (top). The New Haven No. 95 black mantel clock (bottom) looks very different but has the same general type of movement.

Fig. 134. The Gilbert strike movement.

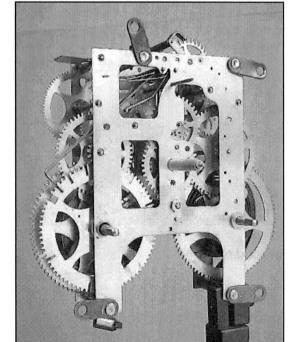

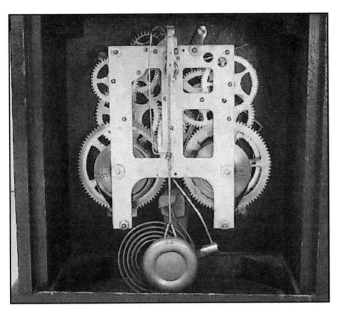

Fig. 135. Rear view of the Gilbert clock with the case back removed.

sional repairers often lament the fact that they spend more time trying to reverse the mistakes made by untrained people than they do performing routine maintenance such as cleaning and oiling. There have been many bad repair attempts uncovered over the years, some as ingenious as they are improper. Sometimes a piece of scrap metal is soldered on the clock plate, next to a worn pivot hole; the metal pushes on the pivot to "restore" its unworn position. At other times someone cuts through the movement plates with a hacksaw to remove the main wheels and springs! These are only two examples of many.

Another disadvantage of eight-day American clocks is that the mainsprings are powerful and can injure the repairer, especially if they are not handled in a safe manner. Chapter 3 gives instructions on how to work on mainsprings.

Technical Features. Someone just completing the repair of an OG clock similar to the one described in the previous section would now find some new challenges in the eight-day Gilbert movement. Mainsprings have already been mentioned, and are perhaps the biggest change.

Like the OG movement, the Gilbert eight-day strike mechanism is also a count wheel type, but it has more parts and the assembly task is more complex. The Gilbert adds a half hour strike; in this case it's a passing strike which does not cause the gear train to run. Other eight-day American strikers have a count wheel designed to make the half hours strike in the same manner as the hours.

The escapement is the recoil strip pallet type, but it is more sensitive to stopping problems than a thirty-hour clock.

Typical Repairs. Eight-day American clocks often have problems in their main wheel assemblies. Broken click springs and clicks are especially common. Chapter 3 provides the details of repairing these parts. Always check the click rivet to make sure it is secure on this type of clock. The thin main wheels may be worn, with the teeth "pocketed" from years of pressure from strong mainsprings. Worn out main wheels may need to be replaced.

Pivots should always be checked for good finish and proper fit in the holes. It is rare that an eight-day American striking clock does not need pivot and bushing work. See Chapter 4.

Escapement problems are common. Always make sure the escape pivots and holes are in good, unworn condition before making adjustments to the escapement. Taking the time to repair and adjust the escapement as described in Chapter 5 will be worth the effort.

Regulating the movement is more difficult than it is with a weight driven unit, since the mainspring drive provides much more power when fully wound than it does on the last few days of the weekly run. It is not unusual for an eight-day American clock to gain several minutes during the first few days, only to lose an equal amount of time as the mainspring runs down.

Fig. 136. American clock parts.

Always disassemble an eight-day striking movement (Figure 136) when repairing it. The chances are that the last three repairers before you did not know how to disassemble, clean and repair the movement properly. Now it's your turn to set things straight.

CUCKOO CLOCK

Cuckoo clocks have been around for hundreds of years. Although many old cuckoo clocks are still with us, the newer ones are much more plentiful. It seems that most homes have a cuckoo clock on the wall and that most of them do not work.

Some may wonder why a clock which symbolizes frustration for some repairers would be suggested here as a good starter clock. The fact is that the cuckoo clock is a good item to try early on. It's likely you'll be handed one as soon as a few people learn that you are working on clocks!

Fig. 137. A modern one-day cuckoo clock.

Cuckoo clocks come in many styles. There are one day and eight-day types, simple cuckoo clocks and fancy ones with complications such as dancing figures, a waterwheel, or a woodcutter who saws away at a log. Each cuckoo clock is basically a house with a bird that emerges to sound his call. With that as the theme, case styles range from the leaf style (Figure 137) to the traditional hunter's clock adorned with a dead bird and rabbit, to an idyllic Swiss chalet with wildflowers and tiny fences. It's probably best to start with a simple modern cuckoo clock such as the one shown.

Advantages. Modern one-day cuckoo clocks are not usually expensive if purchased used and in need of repair. Virtually all the parts are available from suppliers. Even complete movements of the correct brand and size are normally available, as are bel-

Fig. 138. This back view shows how the bellows are installed at the sides of the case.

lows tops, cuckoo birds, pendulums, and carved top ornaments. This makes them attractive as starter clocks.

Disadvantages. Modern cuckoo clock movements were not made to last for generations. A replacement movement may cost only $35.00. It is therefore a sensible repair practice to replace worn-out movements rather than working on them. The original modern movements are repaired if they need only cleaning or if the repairer simply wants to do the restoration.

Fig. 139. The bellows tops are shown mounted on the whistles. Replacement bellows tops are also shown.

Fig. 140. The Hubert Herr cuckoo clock movement.

Technical Features. The modern one-day cuckoo clock movement is weight driven with the weights supported on chains. Most often it has a rack and snail striking movement, in contrast to the count wheel movements featured so far in this chapter. The strike mechanism is a three-note sequence. First, the hammer strikes the gong; then the two bellows lift wires are raised one after the

Figure 141. The wooden leaf style pendulum.

other to blow air into the wooden whistles and simulate the cuckoo bird's call. For 12 o'clock the cuckoo clock sounds "gong-coo-coo" twelve times! A mechanism holds the door open and pushes out the bird during the strike sequence. The right-hand bellows has a lift wire attached which raises the bird's tail with each call.

Typical Repairs. Cleaning and oiling are always needed in the modern cuckoo movement that has been working for years. An inspection will most likely

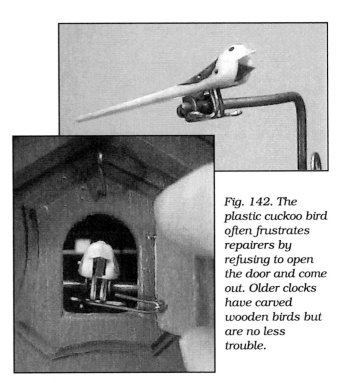

Fig. 142. The plastic cuckoo bird often frustrates repairers by refusing to open the door and come out. Older clocks have carved wooden birds but are no less trouble.

reveal several badly worn pivot holes that will each require a bushing. The ratchets in the chainwheel assemblies sometimes fail. These can sometimes be repaired, but it is a good idea to check with suppliers to see whether the particular assembly you need is still available.

Cuckoo clock strike mechanisms vary from one manufacturer to the next. Study each movement carefully before taking it apart. The movements can be difficult to assemble, so one could consider them good practice for other work to come. Once the simple one-day cuckoo clock is mastered, move up to a musical cuckoo clock.

Fig. 143. The plastic cuckoo clock dial and hands.

The 400-DAY CLOCK

Fig. 144. A Schatz 400-day clock.

The 400-day or anniversary clock was made in huge numbers following World War II. Although finally discontinued in favor of quartz models, the keywind 400-day clock is still abundant, making it a good value for the beginning repairer.

The clock (Figure 144) has a torsion pendulum that rotates on a thin, flat wire suspension spring. The pendulum oscillates only six or eight times a minute, depending on the model. The movement is supported on a baseplate mounted on top of two decorative brass columns. The base is lacquered brass. A glass or plastic dome covers the clock and keeps all parts in full view. The clock can run a full year on one winding.

Advantages. The 400-day clock is a timepiece movement without strike or chime—with few exceptions. This means there are relatively few parts to assemble. Some parts, such as suspension springs and mainsprings, are available from suppliers. A classic book, Charles Terwilliger's *The Horolovar 400-Day Clock Repair Guide*, provides specific information on most 400-day models ever produced.

Disadvantages. Some repairers stay away from the 400-day clock because it is delicate and sometimes defies even the most determined efforts at

repair. In particular, the pivots of the escape arbor and pallet arbor are very fine and must be handled especially carefully. Although it is relatively simple in construction, the 400-day clock requires a high standard of cleanliness and must be properly adjusted if it is to run at all.

Technical Features. The 400-day clock is powered by a barreled mainspring. The escapement is the deadbeat type. Regulation of the clock is based on using the correct thickness of suspension wire in a correctly assembled suspension unit. Each clock has only one specific suspension spring that will run it at the correct rate.

Typical Repairs. Many different repairs may be called for, but cleaning and lubrication, followed by replacement and adjustment of the pendulum suspension unit, are at the top of the list. These tasks are essential because the clock will not run if it is extremely dirty or if the escapement does not function properly.

One of the early steps is to let down the mainspring with a let-down key. The mainspring is powerful, so be careful. After the mainspring is let down, the hands and dial are removed. When you remove the hands, carefully save any washers located under the minute hand nut. The same holds true for a washer under the cannon pinion, if there is such a washer in your clock. These items are necessary for hand tension.

Remove the movement from its platform, then separate the plates and take out all the wheels. Always check for rough pivots and polish away any marks. You will rarely find worn pivot holes in a 400-day clock, but if you suspect there are burrs in a hole corresponding to a rough pivot, clean out the hole with a smoothing broach followed by a toothpick. Proceed to clean and dry the entire movement.

Fig. 145. This close-up of the back of the movement shows the ratchet wheel, click, and click spring.

As part of this process, remove the mainspring from the barrel with a mainspring winder. Never skip the step of cleaning the mainspring. No matter how clean and well adjusted the rest of the movement may be, a dirty mainspring can stop the clock.

Carefully reassemble the wheels between the plates. Do not force any of the pivots into the holes. Leave the pallet unit aside initially, but install the ratchet wheel and other winding parts (Fig. 145) and tighten the pillar nuts. Wind the ratchet only a few clicks and check to be sure that the escape wheel starts up immediately and spins without binding. Let the power down again and install the pallet unit.

Before installing the pallet unit (sometimes called the anchor in these clocks) you should check the tightness of the anchor pin (Figure 146).

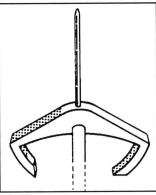

Fig. 146. The anchor assembly (pallet unit).

Some pins are threaded and only need to be tightened. Others may need to be staked in tighter, but soldering is to be discouraged for this repair.

Finish the assembly (Figure 147) and wind the clock about halfway. Install a new suspension spring if needed. The procedure takes only a few minutes to do with the Terwilliger book used as a pattern.

Start the clock running and set the escapement in beat. Figure 148 illustrates the main parts of the suspension unit; the beat is set by turning the saddle in the suspension bracket until the pendulum shows equal overswing following the "tick" on each pallet. After the clock has run for an hour or so, recheck the beat of the escapement and adjust it again if necessary. Watch for a jerky motion of the anchor pin as the clock runs; this can be caused by the fork being set too high on the suspension spring. The opposite problem is an occasional rapid fluttering of the escapement when the anchor pin is in the center of its travel. This is caused by the fork being too low. Intermittent fluttering makes the clock jump ahead several minutes each time it happens, and it can be very difficult to spot. Note: a normal escapement will flutter if the hands are being turned when the anchor pin reaches the center position.

The width of the fork is critical at the point it touches the anchor pin. If the slot is too wide, it causes power to be wasted and the clock may stop. The clock may also stop if the slot is too narrow and binds the anchor pin at any point of its travel.

Escapement adjustments for this clock are cov-

Fig. 147. Rear quarter view showing the back plate and the gears between the plates.

ered in a comprehensive manner in the Terwilliger book. Generally avoid making any depth adjustment to the deadbeat escapement unless there are scratches or other evidence that someone has made an incorrect adjustment that needs to be corrected.

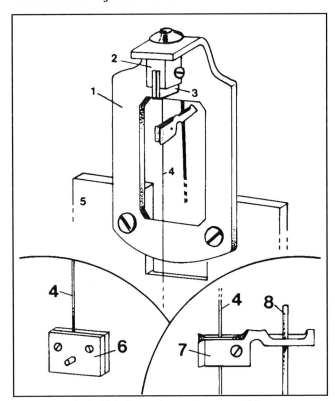

Fig. 148. A 400-day suspension assembly:
1 *suspension bracket;* **2** *saddle;* **3** *top block;*
4 *suspension spring;* **5** *back plate;* **6** *bottom block;*
7 *fork; and* **8** *anchor pin.*

MODERN MANTEL CLOCK WITH HERMLE CHIME MOVEMENT

Fig. 149. Howard Miller #612-300 Westminster chime bracket clock with Hermle movement #340-020.

Some of the best movements to use for learning the basics of chime clock repair are made by Hermle. Learning to service these movements will have an immediate benefit to the beginner, who will often be asked to repair them. Figure 149 shows a Howard Miller clock fitted with a Hermle #340-020 mantel clock movement. Similar Hermle mechanisms are also found in a number of mantel, wall, and grand-father clocks with brand names such as Seth Thomas, Hamilton, and Ridgeway. For many years, Hermle has retained the same style of chime and strike mechanisms on most of its chime movements. Figure 150 shows the #340-020 movement from the Howard Miller clock.

Advantages. The ready availability of Hermle replacement parts is a safety net for anyone who may be concerned about damaging movements during the learning process. In addition, worn Hermle movements are available from suppliers or from other clockmakers who have replaced movements in customers' clocks. These movements are an excellent source of parts, and they offer a stress-free way of learning to disassemble, clean, and reassemble a chime movement. Complete new replacement movements are also available from suppliers.

Disadvantages. A chime movement such as the Hermle is more complex than the movements covered so far in this chapter. Reassembly and adjustment will take longer and require more skill. Another point to be made is that the mainsprings, especially the chime mainspring, are powerful and should be handled with a mainspring winder.

The hobbyist may want to do whatever is necessary to repair a Hermle #340-020 movement, since the parts are available. The professional knows, however, that when a customer is being charged for the work it is sometimes better to replace the entire movement. Replacement is especially recommended over repair when the cost of replacement parts such as mainsprings, barrels, wheels, and the balance unit add up to too much additional expense.

Technical Features. The Hermle #340-020

Fig. 150. Front view (left) and rear view (right) of the Hermle chime movement #340-020. This example was manufactured in 1990 and includes the flat hairspring balance which superseded the popular floating balance.

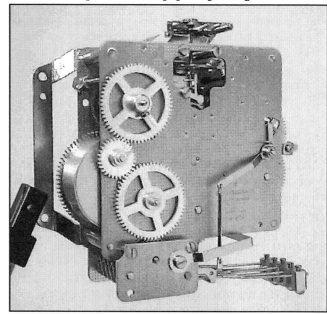

movement featured in this section is an eight-day, three-train, spring driven, Westminster chime clock movement. Figure 151 shows a closer view of the chime and strike parts on the front of the movement. The chime is controlled with a locking plate; the strike mechanism is the rack and snail type. The balance unit is the newer flat hairspring style Hermle has used since discontinuing the floating balance in the late 1980's.

Typical Repairs. Hermle #340-020 movements less than five years old can generally be lubricated and placed back in service. The complaint which brings them in for service within this time period is generally slow chiming or stopping. Use clock oil on the pivots and clock grease for the hammer tails, hammer dampers and certain other parts. The balance pivots can be lubricated with watch oil. See Chapter 8 for more information on lubrication.

Hermle #340-020 movements which are dirty or more than five years old should be disassembled and cleaned before being lubricated. Generally it is not necessary to remove the gathering pallet or the cannon pinion, so the gathering arbor and the center arbor will remain with the front plate. Inspect the movement to locate any worn parts; some Hermle movements, especially those made in the late 1970's, have suffered early wear-out of certain pivot holes. If the wear has occurred at the second arbor locations (above the barrels) these wheel and arbor assemblies should be replaced. The old second arbor pivots should not be polished and reused because problems inherent in the steel will cause the rapid wear of pivot holes to repeat itself. Other specific repair and service problems on these movements are mastered only with experience.

When the movement is to be cleaned, always use a mainspring winder to remove the three mainsprings from the barrels for inspection and cleaning. Replace any damaged or weak mainspring with a new one of the correct Hermle number that you will find stamped on the barrel cover. An alternate service procedure is to order a replacement barrel unit complete with a new mainspring.

The following is a condensed version of the major steps required to assemble and adjust the Hermle #340-020 movement. When the movement is clean and ready to be reassembled, place all the arbors into the front plate. Leave out the balance assembly and the mainspring barrels at this stage. Fit the pivots carefully into their holes, adding the pallet arbor last, and tighten the pillar nuts finger tight. Add the front and rear pivot hole covers for the pallet arbor after oiling the pivots.

Assemble the strike parts first. Turn the strike train wheels with finger pressure and observe the action. The strike hammers should not be engaged

when the strike train stops at the end of a cycle. If it is engaged, the strike will have to start up under load each time. Assuming the gathering pallet was not removed and still remains firmly staked onto the pivot, it will be necessary to separate the plates just enough to allow adjustment. Disengage the third wheel from the pinion on the gathering arbor. Re-index these gears, get the pivots back in the holes, and try the gear train again. When the strike train operates and locks correctly, the adjustment of the hammer rest position is complete.

Fig. 151. The front movement parts.

Add the chime parts next. Figure 151 shows the appearance of the front movement parts of the Hermle #340-020. The pillar nuts can be tightened and the mainspring barrels added and partially wound up for testing purposes.

Figure 152 is a drawing of the chime parts mounted on the front of the movement. Chime counting, locking, and correction are all easy to observe from the front. All chime adjustments, in fact, can be made from the front of the assembled

Fig. 152. Detail view of Hermle front chime parts.

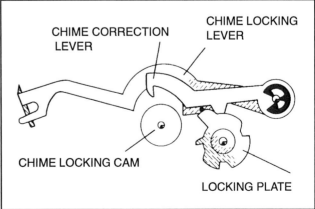

movement. It is not necessary to partially separate the clock plates and change the mesh of a gear with its matching pinion.

Chime locking is accomplished on the chime locking cam (see Figure 152). This is a disk with a pin that faces inward toward the front clock plate. Each quarter hour it captures the chime locking lever to stop the gear train. Chime note counting is done by the locking plate. A raised portion on the hour segment of the locking plate provides the lifting action to unlock the hour strike.

Like the strike mechanisms covered in Chapter 7, the Hermle movement has a warning pin which must be properly set. When the chime train is locked after a run, the warning pin (fixed to a wheel) should be oriented at a 1 o'clock position when viewed from the front. Since the locking cam is held in place with a set screw, it is easy to adjust the warning action. The locking plate is also held by a set screw, making adjustments just as easy to accomplish.

To adjust the chime train, first set the chime warning wheel with the warning pin oriented to a 1 o'clock position as viewed from the front. Now set the chime locking pin and cam against the notch in the chime locking lever (see Figure 152). Tighten the set screw to fasten the cam in place. Next, set the locking plate so the pin on the chime locking lever is in one of the four slots. Tighten the set screw to fasten the locking plate. Finally, add the chime correction lever and fasten with a spring clip. You will then have assembled the chime train in the locked position with the warning correctly set.

Install the minute wheel, hour wheel and snail, and the strike rack. Before putting the washer and spring clip over the minute wheel pinion, check the snail position. Do this by turning the minute hand through several quarters, waiting each time for the gear train to function. If the rack tail drops correctly to permit 12 o'clock and 1 o'clock striking, the adjustment is right.

Install the hammer assembly underneath the movement. Hook on the connecting link between

Fig. 153. The chime drive wheel (top) is located on the back of the movement and is held in place with a set screw.

the strike hammers and the hammer-lift arm.

Add the large chime drive wheel (Fig. 153) on the elongated rear pivot of the third chime arbor. A small and large wheel are now added below to transmit power to the pin barrel. The chime hammers must be set to the correct sequence. Turn the minute hand through a full hour, until you have completed the four-note chime at the first quarter. Loosen the set screw on the chime drive wheel, then turn it counterclockwise by hand. This will operate the hammers independently of the gear train. After you see the four chime hammers rise and fall in order from front to rear, the adjustment is done. Tighten the set screw on the chime drive wheel, but do not overtighten it because a burr can be raised by the pointed screw, making future adjustments impossible. Operate the chimes to make sure the hammers operate correctly and never stop in the raised position at the end of any chime sequence.

It is hoped that the "starter" clocks featured in this chapter will encourage new repairers to go out and find clocks to study and repair. By choosing your clocks wisely, you can have fun and learn at the same time.

APPENDIX A

ADJUSTING THE CRUTCH
SETTING THE CLOCK IN BEAT

S etting a clock running can be an exciting moment—whether you've finally completed many hours of restoration work or just arrived home with a flea market "find". Small details sometimes make a big difference in getting the clock started.

This Appendix covers two adjustments that are small but important: adjusting the crutch and setting the pendulum beat. Both involve the pendulum assembly and both are critical to the running of the clock.

Adjusting the Crutch

The crutch is a critical part of the escapement in a pendulum clock. Although the crutch comes in several forms, its purpose is always the same: to transmit the impulse from the pallets to the pendulum rod. (In modern movements, the pendulum rod is a different type called the pendulum leader.)

A loss of power always results during the transfer of the impulse from the crutch to the pendulum. If the crutch is worn, dirty, or poorly adjusted, the loss may be great enough to stop the clock. Even if the clock does run, its performance is affected. The arc of the pendulum swing is smaller than it should be, making the clock subject to stopping after the slightest disturbance.

Wire loop crutch. Figure 154 shows the most common type of crutch on American striking clock. It is made from a brass wire formed into a loop at the lower end. The pendulum rod passes through

Fig. 154. The pendulum rod passes vertically through the wire crutch loop in this Ingraham movement.

the loop. At the end of the loop the wire is tapered thin and is easily bent. The rod should pass freely through the slot, not binding or resting at either end of the slot. There must be clearance between the rod and the sides of the slot. If this clearance is too great, the crutch "kicks", losing much of the thrust it receives from the pallets.

There are a few adjustments which need to be made to the crutch. These adjustments are routine and sometimes take only a few minutes to do. Figure 155 shows a correctly fitted crutch on the left. The sides of the slot are parallel with enough clear-

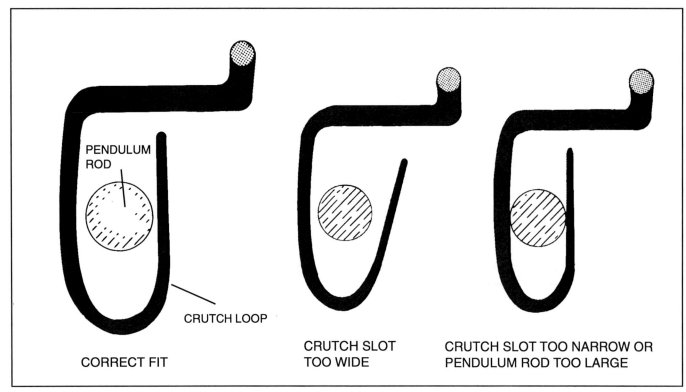

PENDULUM ROD

CRUTCH LOOP

CORRECT FIT

CRUTCH SLOT TOO WIDE

CRUTCH SLOT TOO NARROW OR PENDULUM ROD TOO LARGE

Fig. 155. Top cross-sectional views of a wire loop crutch such as the Ingraham.

ance for the pendulum rod to pass through.

The center view in the drawing shows a wire loop crutch slot that is too wide and too narrow at the same time. The slot is widened at the open end, and if the pendulum rod passes through in this area there will be a loss of power. If the case is moved or tilted, however, the rod will move to the front and be captured by the closed end of the slot. The binding which results will stop the clock.

The right-hand drawing shows what happens when a replacement rod of larger diameter is installed in the clock. The sides of the slot are parallel but too narrow. The rod will bind and probably stop the clock.

The crutch slot can be reshaped if a piece of steel rod slightly larger in diameter than the pendulum rod is inserted in the slot. The crutch loop is formed around this rod and the sides are made parallel. The slot will now be a good fit for the pendulum rod and will not bind at any point.

Flat brass crutch. Many other clocks have a crutch made from a piece of flat brass. The slot in the crutch may be closed, in which case the pendulum rod or leader must be slipped into it from above or below. The slot may also be designed with a narrow cut through which the pendulum leader can be angled. The flat crutch is stronger than a wire loop crutch and is less likely to become distorted.

The closed loop type is found in a movement such as the Seth Thomas No. 124 chime. This slot is

durable and rarely needs to be made wider or narrower. Widening can be done by filing the sides of the slot. Narrowing is difficult to accomplish, since any attempt to close the slot (for example, with pliers) is likely to crush the piece. Perhaps the clock has a pendulum rod that can be replaced with one of smaller diameter.

Figure 156 shows the crutch from a Hermle grandfather clock movement. It is an open-slot type with an opening to the side and rear that permits the insertion of the flat pendulum leader. The leader connects the suspension spring and the pendulum. This slot can be adjusted with a lever, but it is important to keep the sides of the slot parallel to avoid causing the pendulum to wobble.

Always check a flat brass crutch by first looking down on the assembly to make sure the crutch is not twisted. Straightening it is better done with the pendulum leader out of the

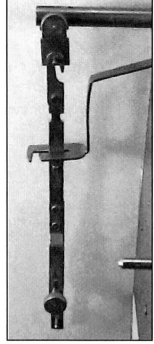

Fig. 156. Hermle crutch.

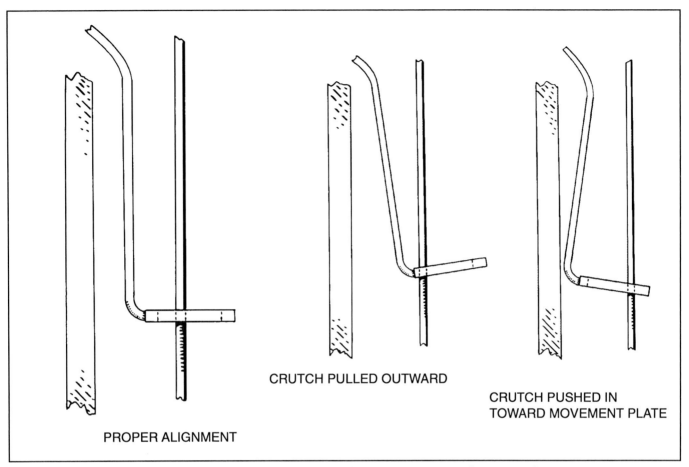

CRUTCH PULLED OUTWARD

CRUTCH PUSHED IN
TOWARD MOVEMENT PLATE

PROPER ALIGNMENT

Fig. 157. Side view of a flat brass style crutch showing correct and incorrect alignments.

clock. This protects the suspension spring from damage.

Next look at the assembly from the side. Figure 157 shows three views of a crutch that could represent almost any brand of clock with a flat crutch. The left-hand view shows that the pendulum rod or leader passes straight through the center of the slot. The other two views show that binding will occur if the crutch has been pulled outward or pushed in toward the movement plate. Remove the pendulum rod before straightening the crutch. It is a simple matter to bend a modern crutch with your fingers. Older movements require more care to make sure the crutch or the rear pallet arbor pivot will not break. If there is any doubt in your mind, let down the power or remove the weights from the clock and then take the pallet unit out. Study the bending which is required and move cautiously.

Another type of crutch is the flat brass type formed without the 90° bend at the end. A steel pin on the pendulum fits through this slot to form a simple, strong arrangement. It is difficult to adjust the alignment of the steel pin unless it points to the side because of a bent suspension spring. The width of the slot can be opened up or squeezed tighter

without too much trouble. Remember to leave some clearance for the pin and to coat it with clock grease.

There are many other variations in crutch design. Urgos, the German manufacturer had its own design that worked quite well and tended to reduce pendulum wobble if it was kept well adjusted. Another German maker, Erhard Jauch, used a design in the 1960's that was particularly difficult to repair because the suspension spring had to be the exact correct length to fit the pendulum suspension unit.

The common denominator in all crutch designs is that they are made to work with some clearance for the pendulum rod or leader. Always check for a bent crutch or ill-fitting rod whenever you work on a pendulum clock. It may be one of the last details you attend to before starting the clock, but it is a critical one.

Setting the Clock in Beat

The subject of bending the crutch brings us to the other topic in this appendix: placing a clock in beat. Most pendulum clocks are quite sensitive to the beat adjustment. It can be a difficult concept to explain to repair customers. I sometimes just say that the clock which is "in beat" ticks with an even rhythm, like a metronome. This analogy doesn't work very well, however, when people concentrate on a slight difference in the tone quality or loudness of the "tick" compared to the "tock"—the sound made at each pallet.

Setting the beat on a clock with a wire loop crutch is shown in Figure 158. The description applies whether you have a between-the-plates type escapement or a front mounted pallet unit.

The first step is to place the clock on a perfectly level table or workbench. Check it front-to-back and side-to-side to be certain. Start the clock ticking

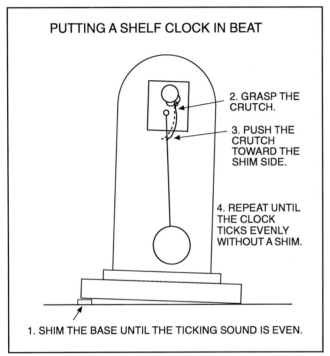

PUTTING A SHELF CLOCK IN BEAT

2. GRASP THE CRUTCH.

3. PUSH THE CRUTCH TOWARD THE SHIM SIDE.

4. REPEAT UNTIL THE CLOCK TICKS EVENLY WITHOUT A SHIM.

1. SHIM THE BASE UNTIL THE TICKING SOUND IS EVEN.

Fig. 158. Diagram showing how to put a clock in beat.

and listen to the sound. Place shims under one or the other side of the base until the ticking sound is even. This shows you how far out of beat the clock is at this stage.

The crutch wire must be bent to correct the beat. When you make the bend in the wire, grip and hold it near the pallets. Pliers are helpful. Make a small bend by pushing lower down on the crutch wire. Push it toward the side of the case that has the shim.

Try removing the shim and checking to see whether the clock is in beat or at least closer to being correct. Shim the clock again and repeat the steps outlined until the clock is in beat.

The idea of bending toward the shim helps to

keep your adjustments moving in the right direction. It isn't necessary to keep shimming the clock case once you have learned which direction to bend the crutch in each instance. Try to avoid random bending or severe changes. Careless bending may have little or no effect or may even have the opposite effect from the one you are seeking.

Flat brass crutches are more difficult to bend, since the flat brass resists changes. Determine first of all whether the crutch is supposed to be bent at all. Some have a slipping clutch at the pallet arbor which makes adjustments easy. Do not simply push the crutch all the way to one extreme or the other to adjust this kind of crutch. Study it first to make sure the pallet unit will not bottom out in the escape wheel and bend a tooth. Some clocks have steady pins set in the back plate on either side of the crutch to prevent this kind of damage. It is usually possible to place your fingers on top of the pallet unit to hold it. Then push on the crutch to change the adjustment.

Most modern grandfather clocks have a self-setting beat mechanism in the pallet unit. It amounts to an extremely loose clutch which allows the assembly to slip while the pendulum has overswing—which it normally does when this type of clock is started up. The slipping finally stops when the pendulum arc is reduced to its working size, leaving the clock in beat. The trouble with this mechanism is that the amount of slippage must be precise. If the slip is excessive, the clock can wander out of beat and stop all by itself, or it can get out of beat whenever the hands are turned. On the other hand, a tight clutch does not set the beat automatically.

Remedies for this type of self-setting beat unit range from gluing the clutch into one piece or taking a lot of trouble to rebuild or re-engineer the pallet unit for correct slippage. It is far better to replace the unit with a new one, which is possible for most movements made with this type of crutch.

Another beat setting device is usually applied to the flat brass crutches which use a steel pin fastened to the pendulum. The pin fits into a knurled disc which can be turned precisely to set the beat very quickly.

Setting the beat on a clock may require a number of attempts, and it sometimes seems almost a trial and error kind of exercise. Practice will improve your skill, and patience helps. Some repairers use a beat amplifier to make the ticking of the clock sound loud enough to hear clearly.

APPENDIX B

GLOSSARY OF CLOCK REPAIR TERMS

T hose who are new to clock repair sometimes need a basic definition or two. This short glossary explains some of the repair terms used in this book and a few others which are not used in the text. Many of the items can also be located in the Index.

A

ANCHOR. The British term for a set of recoil pallets. Also used to identify the deadbeat pallets in a 400-day clock.

ANNEAL. To soften steel by heating it in a flame and allowing it to cool slowly.

ARBOR. The shaft or axle of a clock upon which a wheel and/or pinion are mounted.

B

BARREL. Tube-shape container for a mainspring. A gear is attached to one end.

BEATS PER HOUR (or MINUTE). The number of swings made by a pendulum in a given period of time; the clock's rate.

BROACH. To enlarge a hole, especially a pivot or bushing hole. Also refers to two tools: the five-sided cutting broach for enlarging the holes and the round smoothing broach for polishing them.

BROCOT. A pin pallet escapement named after its inventor. A. Brocot also invented a type of pendulum suspension device used in French clocks.

BUSHING. A bearing or sleeve pressed into a clock plate to replace a worn pivot hole.

C

CHIME. A melody played on metal rods or tubular bells at regular intervals, usually each quarter hour. Most chimes are based on cathedral melodies for particular churches in England.

CLICK. Clockmaker's term for the pawl which engages the ratchet wheel to hold the power of the mainspring or weight.

CLICK SPRING. A piece of steel or brass spring wire or flat stock which seats the click in the ratchet wheel.

COUNT WHEEL. A device which is slotted to receive a lever which signals the end of each strike sequence.

CRUTCH. A brass rod or flat brass piece extending from the pallet arbor to connect it to the swinging pendulum.

D

DEADBEAT. An escapement invented by George Graham in 1715. As an escape tooth touches on the locking faces of a pallet, the escape wheel remains "dead" until impulse occurs on the impulse face of the pallet.

E

ENDSHAKE. The front-to-back freedom of movement characteristic of a clock arbor fitted between two movement plates and essential for smooth running of the arbor.

ESCAPEMENT. The device in a clock which allows the gearing to move ahead in definite, controlled movements.

F

FUSEE. A cone-shaped device mounted on the same arbor with the great wheel in some clocks, equalizing the pull of the mainspring barrel over the running time of the clock.

G

GATHERING PALLET. A part which moves ahead the strike (or chime) rack as the various strokes or notes are counted.

GEAR. Any toothed wheel used in clockwork.

H

HALF-DEADBEAT. A variation on the deadbeat escapement in which the locking faces of the pallets are not drawn as arcs from the pallet arbor center. The design causes some recoil to occur.

HOROLOGY. The study, design, construction, or repair of the devices (clocks or watches) used to measure and indicate the passage of time.

L

LATHE. A machine tool capable, depending on the type, of making clock parts by rotating the parts to be shaped by tool bits or other cutters.

LET-DOWN KEY. A smooth-handled clock key made for the safe release of mainspring power in a clock.

M

MAINSPRING. A coiled, flat spring used to power a train of gears in a clock or watch.

MAINSPRING "BOX". Term which refers to a cylindrical retainer for a mainspring; it is fastened to the clock plate and does not rotate like a barrel.

MOTION WORK. The set of gears which drives the hands in a clock.

O

OG. A rectangular style of American shelf clock from the 19th century; the term refers to the name for the curved molding on the front of the case.

P

PALLET. Hardened steel piece which accepts impulse from the escape wheel teeth.

PINION. The small toothed member usually driven by a wheel in a clock.

PIVOT. The end of an arbor which is reduced to a smaller diameter to permit it to rotate in the pivot hole in the movement plate.

PULLEY. A grooved wheel which supports a cable and weight in a clock; used to direct the movement of the cable and placement of the weight or additionally as a simple machine to lessen the weight fall required for a specified run time.

R

RACK. A ratchet-toothed piece which is used as a counting device in striking and chiming clocks.

RACK HOOK. A piece which rests between rack teeth to hold the rack in position.

RATCHET. A toothed wheel used in conjuction with a click (pawl) to hold back a mainspring and permit winding.

RECOIL. A type of escapement in use since about 1660; the shape of the pallet unit causes the escape wheel to reverse direction (recoil) briefly before giving impulse to the pallets.

REGULATOR. An accurate, well-made clock; often incorrectly applied, even by manufacturers, to ordinary household clocks as a description of quality.

REPIVOTING. A repair procedure in which a damaged pivot is removed, the arbor drilled, and a new pivot inserted.

S

STRIKE. The sounding of notes to announce (typically) the hour and half hour.

SNAIL. A stepped or (in some French clocks) smooth spiral shape which determines the duration of striking or chiming which is to occur.

STOP-WORKS. A pair of meshing gears which are designed to limit mainspring usage or weight travel.

T

TIMEPIECE. A clock which does not strike or chime.

V

VERGE. An antique clock escapement predating the recoil and deadbeat; in the U.S., the pallet unit of any clock.

VULLIAMY. Type of deadbeat pallet unit with adjustable pallets, named for its inventor.

W

WARNING. A short run of a strike or chime train which poises it to unlock quickly and begin playing at the correct moment; present in most, but not all, clocks with strike or chime mechanisms.

WHEEL. A clock gear distinguished from a pinion.

INDEX